MY FRIEND ROBESPIERRE

THE DEATH MASK OF MAXIMILIEN ROBESPIERRE.

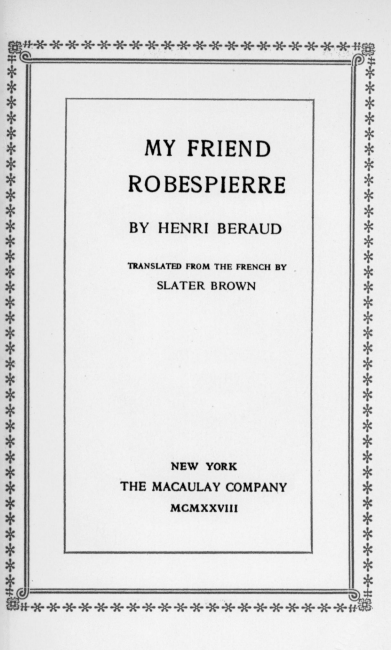

MY FRIEND ROBESPIERRE

BY HENRI BERAUD

TRANSLATED FROM THE FRENCH BY

SLATER BROWN

NEW YORK
THE MACAULAY COMPANY
MCMXXVIII

PRINTED IN THE UNITED STATES OF AMERICA

ILLUSTRATIONS

MY FRIEND ROBESPIERRE

PROLOGUE

On the tenth Pluviose, 1795, as evening gathered, a man slowly picked his way through the mud of that section in Paris called Petite-Pologne. He was respectably dressed in a cloak of ratine; in his hand he held a small bunch of flowers. The paling he followed led him to a large, unwieldy gate on which some one had scribbled the word, "*Dormir*."

The stranger, as if the place were familiar to him, pushed the gate open and entered a kind of enclosed cemetery. Two elms, their lower trunks encrusted with blackened moss, leaned over the moldy, lime-strewn soil. Under the leafless branches of these trees the visitor halted and took off his hat. After standing a moment in meditation, he laid the flowers on the ground; then, as the misty darkness thickened around him, he crossed himself furtively, and without hesitating longer, he departed. Skirting the edge of the Parc Monceau he soon gained Faubourg Saint-Honoré. Heavy drops of rain began to fall. A lamplighter came, carrying his flickering torch from post to post. Already the doors of theaters and dance halls were opening.

The solitary visitor was I. And the mournful grave

to which, braving universal reprobation, I had brought my pledge of loyalty was that of my boyhood friend, Maximilien Robespierre.

That was just thirty years ago.

And today, the twenty-sixth of January, 1825, as I begin my memoirs of the Incorruptible, my thoughts revert to that same sad evening in the third winter of the Republic. Once more I hear gusts of wind shaking the bare branches of the two elms over the graves of Danton and Robespierre.

Thirty years ago! And what have those thirty years left us now of all that strife and death? Nothing. Not an earthly sign. And what remains of those two men and all their genius? A handful of laws, the echoes of an outworn eloquence, the lies teachers will from age to age repeat to their pupils.

Under the floor of a common dance hall, their ashes now lie forgotten.

How far off it seems. We are now in the year of grace 1825. And Charles X, surrounded on the steps of his throne with cardinals and nobles in silk stockings, directs a search for the Holy Phial which an enthusiastic sansculotte smashed with his hammer thirty years ago in the Place de Reims.

And what have I become? I am a magistrate in the royal court of justice. Yes, I, the friend of Robespierre, the confidant of his youth at Arras, I, a judge! I sit at court surrounded by eight thousand volumes of laws. I am sixty-five years old. My hair is white. I have learned something about men, and I have memories enough and to spare.

But it is not my own story I tell. . . .

Six months after the death of Robespierre, I was one of three to visit the last remains of the man who had held all France at his feet; the others were a woman in black, and a man, whose face was careworn. The woman in mourning, whom I knew well, was Robespierre's betrothed. The man, an unknown disciple, was devoured with remorse for not having followed his master to the tomb. By chance the three of us would occasionally meet before the gate. We would exchange a few words then. But these brief occasional meetings did not suffice us. Soon it appeared good and proper for us to gather around a few relics, that we might better evoke the memory of him whom the vigilance of spies constrained us to mourn in secret. Our hearts were full of him, but as our memories touched separate phases of his life, the outline of his character assumed a different aspect for each of us. I alone, perhaps, of all three knew there were both weakness and tenderness in Maximilien. Certain confessions are made only when hearts are young.

So did lover, disciple and friend share these sad pleasures. Forced to fuse our impressions, we no longer tried to keep them separate, but let them unite in a single image. The life of Maximilien Robespierre, which I now write, occasionally seems to me a memorial of these reunions, in which our pious faith fought the eternal shadows for this orphan of Arras, this penniless deputy, this statesman.

Must I present an exact picture of his character? Alas, what do we know even of those who are dearest and closest to us? Does not the most life-like portrait possess in the last analysis only the value of an awkward and halting witness?

I wish to tell what I know. I wish to describe this great citizen as I have seen him, and to that purpose I will turn to reason for those painful truths my heart may refuse to grant me. For Robespierre's memory would not tolerate a false benevolence of praise, comparable to the rouge embalmers smear on the cheeks of the dead. Indeed, Robespierre would consider a complaisant friend an unworthy friend. And if this book had need of an epigraph, Maximilien has already shown it to me in Pascal: "Few friendships would endure could we but know what our friends say of us when we are gone—even though they spoke it sincerely and dispassionately."

I write only to be sincere. That alone can give value to my memoirs. I do not propose to be a guide for future historians of the Revolution, nor to refute the first volumes of that history Messrs. Thiers and Bodin are at this very moment publishing. Nor do I intend, moreover, to denounce the writings of that miserable Delaure, who dares to present my friend as the paid tool of foreigners.

Indeed, what do these eminent but prejudiced writers know of the man whose memory they condemn? Better would it be for them, for the public, and for truth itself, had they known only the true color of his eyes, shared the dreams of his youth, or even suffered the fearful abstractions of his soul. Thus, and thus only, could they have been able to decide—in the words Maximilien sometimes borrowed from his master Rousseau—whether Nature had done well or ill to break the mold in which she had cast him.

Paris, the twenty-ninth of January, 1825.

BOOK ONE

CHAPTER ONE

My father, who was clerk of the criminal court, lived in the center of Arras, in that damp quarter called Murs-Saint-Waast. His huge, gloomy house was bare of furniture, but full of echoes. In that part of the city the streets twist every twenty paces, and they are so narrow you can cross them in a stride.

At a little distance from us, there was another house. It was more impressive than ours, with five windows to every floor, and a mansard roof. Four steps, green with moss, led from the front door to the street.

M. François Derobespierre, who lived in this house, was a lawyer in the provincial court of Artois. He was a queer, unhappy man. Far back in my memory I see him, with his lace shirt, his black clothes, and his powdered periwig. Every forenoon he returned from court and would stop for a moment or two in the center of the square that in those days served as a fish market. It was there his son and I shared our games with a few lads of the neighborhood.

Arras in those days was not what it is now. A criminal vandalism had not yet mutilated its buildings. There were churches, abbeys, chapels, asylums, convents; and the carillons in the belfries made gay music. Sometimes the great Bancloque would ring with such mighty strokes it seemed to shake the sky. And horsemen wearing fatigue caps would file past slowly, to exercise their horses along the banks of the Scarpe. They would return through the lower part of the city, to those barracks from which the sound of bells rose in the morning.

Almost every day at noon M. Derobespierre would return from court. With scarcely a good-by to us, little Maximilien would run to greet his father as soon as he saw him. As I remember, this scene invariably took place in silence. M. Derobespierre would take his son's hand. After walking a few steps, they would disappear into their house and the door would close upon them.

Soon our two families were drawn into close friendship. My father's work led him to court. As to M. Derobespierre, he went to court every day without fail, whether to plead a case, or whether, after the custom of lawyers, merely to stroll to and fro in the corridors. The two men met each other every day, and developed a neighborly friendship. Soon they began walking home together. One morning on the way home my father admitted he cherished the hope of making me a lawyer.

"I am delighted to hear it," our neighbor exclaimed good-naturedly. "Maximilien will then have his boyhood friend as fellow scholar and comrade. For if it please God, my oldest son will also be a lawyer to take my place at the bar, and our two sons can pursue their careers together."

"My family would feel honored, indeed," said my father, and he added, "I would give everything I own to make my son a lawyer."

I had a brother named Tiburce whose existence I must touch upon in a few words, as he has a rôle to play in this story. Tiburce was sixteen years my senior. They called him Iron Head. After many escapades, he bade farewell to his legal studies and his family, and left for Paris to seek his fortune among crooks and adventurers. At this period I was still a small boy. For a long time we were without news of him and my poor mother, who had a weakness for the rascal, died without ever seeing him again. My father never mentioned his name. However, as we shall see, Tiburce was to make his way in the world.

But to return to the story. I was at that time the hope and consolation of my family. In speaking about me to M. Derobespierre, my father had opened up his heart. Though M. Derobespierre may have thought to himself that my father's ambition, however praiseworthy, would entail heavy sacrifices, his estimation of the honest clerk was greatly increased.

I believe, if my memory does not fail me, that the first invitation to our neighbors' house followed my father's confession of his ambition. At any rate, it was about this time that I first saw Maximilien's mother.

Mme. Derobespierre was frail, pretty, of distinguished appearance. She was the daughter of a brewer in the suburb of Rouville, by name Carrault. Of her humble birth, however, she preserved only a lively sympathy for the sufferings of the common people. Her husband's family of strict-laced lawyers had received her very coldly at first, persuaded by their own bourgeois prejudices that the young man had married beneath him. But the fresh and delicate charm of the young woman soon overcame all resistance.

No woman has ever appeared sweeter to me. She spoke so tenderly to her children, maintaining a kind of fairy-like power over them. Indeed she had that charm peculiar to certain young mothers which stamps the minds of children so profoundly that later when they become men and women they can never remember it except with the deepest emotion.

She received me with a thousand caresses, and at once led me upstairs to the room the younger children lived in. The last child was still in his cradle. It was Augustin. Two girls, Charlotte, who was five, and her sister Henriette, who was two years younger, both dressed in frocks of fustian and innumerable ribbons, were playing dolls on an upholstered couch. A fifth child died at birth.

Maximilien had never mentioned his brother and little sisters and I was unaware of their existence. Was his silence due to dissimulation, jealousy, indifference? Not at all. It was, and I most clearly understand it now, an early sign of that extremely English reticence he observed throughout his life toward everything that was by its nature private or personal. Never did a being in this world display less need of opening up his heart. This excessive reserve often sharpened his sufferings to the raw edge of despair. It was inherited, I believe, from his father, who, alas, was soon to let reticence devour his mind. . . . But do not let us anticipate.

CHAPTER TWO

MAXIMILIEN was two years older than I. But being of a delicate constitution, he grew slowly, while I grew like a weed. As a result we were about the same height.

You could already observe something impenetrable about him, an over-seriousness that awed the other children. During our games, doubtless because his voice was feeble, he never shouted.

But what the good people of our neighborhood remarked upon most often was the pale, steel color of his eyes. Maximilien lowered these strange eyes of his only before his father. It often happened that grown-ups, meeting his glance, would turn away with a certain uneasiness, with a certain agitation they could not master. My poor mother said, "That child has eyes that look into your very soul." She did not care for him.

So far as that went, this simple woman expressed the sentiment of everyone. One can say that from his infancy Maximilien was condemned to the prison of his own heart. Never did he awake in others that warm and spontaneous sympathy nature grants to the larger portion of mankind. The sentiment he aroused from his earliest boyhood was a feeling in which hostility, submission and esteem were mixed. No confidence, no tenderness, was ever given him. His heart very soon closed, and among his noisy companions, always eager to share their little secrets, he at an early age formed the habit of keeping his impressions to himself.

At that time he made no exception save with me. And even this was not due to any predilection of his own. He himself had not chosen me. His parents visited mine, and during those gloomy provincial calls they sent us out to play in the garden. Maximilien accepted me then as a playmate, and as I yielded to him in everything, he did not delay in displaying affection for me.

To-day, after these sixty years, I see him as he was then, on the verge of that unhappiness which was to bear down so profoundly upon his life and his character.

He was delicate, and of small stature. His face was white and heavy, his nose pointed, his mouth very large, while his hands—a rare thing among us ragamuffins—were always clean.

His mother dressed him with care. He wore a frogged and braided coat, with a collar of mousseline, white stockings and buckled shoes. The fear of spoiling his clothes made him awkward even in his play, a certain awkwardness of movement and gesture he never overcame. Thus the attention Robespierre never failed to give his appearance dates from the very earliest days of his life: a fastidiousness for which the red-capped demagogues reproached him with such coarse bitterness when he had risen above them into power.

All this, that air, that seriousness, those eyes of his, are so singular in a child that after these many years I question my memory. Might I not be the victim of some illusion born of the very remoteness of that time? Do not the man and child fuse in my memory? Do I not attribute to the young boy of Arras certain traits which belong only to the member of the National Convention? But no. A thousand details reaffirm my memory, and my old contemporaries at Arras who at the time of Louis XV lived in the quarter of Saint-Waast retain a similar picture of the little Derobespierre. It will soon be seen that such really was his nature. Other circumstances will prove the truth of it.

I remember that about this time the Derobespierres received constant visits from a dignified gentleman to whom the shopkeepers respectfully raised their hats as he passed. The visits of this man filled me with curiosity. But to all questions I asked about him, my parents would reply only:

"You are not old enough to understand."

But I noticed their sadness. They darkly mentioned "that poor little woman," saying the merciful God in his divine wisdom often showed Himself very harsh to even the best of families. It happened also that M. Derobespierre, returning from court one day with my father, paused a moment before our house. I saw him wipe away tears from his eyes. Tears in so stern and reserved a man overwhelmed me. That evening my parents talked to each other in low voices. Then I saw my mother put a scarf over her head and go out. She returned at supper time, with reddened eyes.

The following day—the 16th of July, 1764, to be exact—it rained steadily from dawn. Towards noon a coach, clattering at full speed over the cobblestones, lunged through our alley, to draw up before the house of the Derobespierres. The horses steamed with sweat. Two men climbed down. I recognized the first as the visitor whom I have already mentioned. It was he who raised the knocker. Then, with great deference, he stepped to one side, and his companion, who wore a long traveling coat, entered the house. I learned later that this stranger was M. de Villois, a well known surgeon, the pupil and assistant of the famous Lieutaud. He had arrived from Amiens by the post chaise, having been called into consultation by his confrère at Arras, M. Warringhe.

Later, when they pushed their way through the crowd of curious who had gathered around the door, they both seemed even more grave. M. Derobespierre accompanied them to the coach. I was shocked by his pallor. He climbed the front steps unsteadily, like a man whose strength betrays him after a long struggle. He watched the mail coach disappear before he reëntered his house.

A little later, to the explosive cracking of a whip, a carriage arrived by way of Rue de St. Jean-en-Rouville. Old man Carrault climbed down, gesticulating and mopping his eyes. He hitched his old mare to a ring in the wall, and showing every sign of despair, he in his turn disappeared through the door. Meanwhile the rain fell. Before evening I was placed trembling in my bed, and I knew nothing more of what happened.

A few days passed. I was kept away from the windows. Though I questioned my parents, it was in vain; I learned nothing of what was going on in our neighbor's house. But the following Sunday, at the church of St. Aubert, Maximilien came dressed all in black. During mass, his eyes, staring into emptiness, saw something other children were not able to see.

CHAPTER THREE

The following months have left me sad, disordered memories through which people prowl like shadows. It was like a series of interminable Sundays: days without play, without end. . . .

The door of the Derobespierre house remained shut. Thereafter my father returned from court alone. The lawyer, stricken with sorrow, lived outside the world, not even going to church. An old servant used to lead Maximilien there, and then hurry him away immediately after the *"Ite missa est."*

But what still appears to me as the most painful thing of all was the tone of mystery the conversation took when someone happened to speak with pity of the widower, in front of me. During these monotonous Sundays when the wind moaned in the chimney or a fine rain beat against the windowpanes, my childish imagination soared. At this age does one know what Death is? In low voices people spoke of Maximilien's young mother, so sweet, so pretty, who had died of consumption. I searched for a hidden meaning in these words, a meaning more terrible than the truth. And I believed in my dream-crowded ignorance that there was something more dreadful than death. Everything surrounding the event, those tears, the tolling of bells, M. Derobespierre's encloistered silence, the black clothes, the funereal whispers, all of it, did it not fortify my belief that death was punishment inflicted by the Creator upon the relatives of the dead? Concealing my trouble, I groped for explanations. Mad fears denied me sleep, and one night I awoke screaming for my mother. It ended by my falling ill, and the grave gentleman, that doctor whom I had but recently seen entering our neighbor's house, I now found one morning beside my own bed, holding my wrist between his fingers. As in a dream, I heard him speaking.

"He must be sent away for a while, Madame," he murmured, shaking his head. "Haven't you some friends or relatives in the country? He is a sensitive child, but nature . . . "

In a fog, I saw my father holding my mother in his arms. Then it seemed as if I fell asleep again. . . .

A few days later, we took the diligence for Maroeil, where my mother's parents lived on a farm.

I stayed there until haying time, when I returned to Arras, healed, washed clean of my fears. In the autumn I was placed in school. I found Maximilien there, grown older, working hard, and being pointed out by the School Fathers as an exemplary student.

Some months passed. Side by side on our bench, we received instruction that was both strict and medieval. My memory of it is a long unbroken stretch of ennui.

CHAPTER FOUR

I WAS never to see M. Derobespierre again, for he, in an excess of despair, had taken the strangest sort of decision. I have already mentioned that at first he closeted himself in his house. Invisible to everyone, he surrendered himself to a somber and silent exaltation. In vain did his friends and those nearest to him seek to draw him from his retreat. The door remained closed to all visitors. It was hoped that time might allay his sorrow. But it did not, indeed, quite the reverse.

By force of living alone and brooding over his suffering, M. Derobespierre ended by deranging his mind. The sight of his children, far from arousing his courage, only more acutely reminded him of his loss. Finally his disorder led him to such a state that one day he rushed to the home of a friend to tell him of his intended departure. His "departure" . . . a better word would be flight. For the widower fled alone to England, leaving his four children on the hands of their grandparents.

Some time later, a gaunt, bewildered man was seen returning to Arras, trying to live again. He appeared at court, wishing to plead. But they say that all his energy seemed broken, and after a week he gave up trying. He disappeared again. This time he left everything behind him, taking only his coat and his cane. Some maintain that he ended his days in Munich. But it has never been proved. A certain Abbé Proyart writes that the desperate man lived a little while in Germany, where he opened a school for children, that he later went to London, and ended by emigrating to the Antilles, where he lived to survive his sons. . . . But no one possesses any certain information either of his death or of his ancestors, which some say came from Ireland. It is known only that he fled, and one accepted this as intelligence of his death.

The day that this news reached school, I was called into the office of M. de la Borère, the principal. Maximilien was there already. The principal said to me:

"Embrace your friend. A great misfortune has just befallen him. He has lost his father. . . ."

At these words I was extremely moved. Holding back my tears with great difficulty, I took my poor friend in my arms. He was unyielding and I saw his eyes were dry.

"Good," said M. de la Borère. "Now leave your unhappy friend and return to your classes."

That same evening Maximilien reappeared among us. Each one of us was struck by his proud and distant manner. His companions were too young to understand what was taking place in this orphan, who, matured so soon by his unhappiness, was so different from other children. He was thought evil. With the cruelty of their age, the pupils united against their unfortunate school fellow, who suffered in silence, refusing to seek their sympathy. They pretended to ignore him, but it was useless. Maximilien, wrapped up in his own reflections, did not notice the plot. Already his heart had adapted itself to solitude, and he was scarcely able to endure my faithfulness. For I still remained loyal to him and did my best to share in his disgrace.

Under the school wall there was a stone bench on which the two of us, side by side, passed our hours of recreation. Maximilien would sit with folded arms and that detached and thoughtful attitude he affected all his life. If he broke the silence, it was to speak to me of his young brother and his sisters. For at nine years he realized that he was head of a family.

A little later his grandfather, the brewer Carrault, arranged to have his little grandson stay with him, and at the same time he took charge of the younger boy, while M. Derobespierre's sisters took charge of the girls.

It was about this time that Maximilien took a fancy to raising birds. The old brewer, who had money and was generous with it, did not deny him this hobby. The little orphan had dovecotes and pigeons. He gave his birds the tenderest care. Every Sunday the carriole came to take me to Rouville, and there Maximilien made me admire his pigeons. One night there was a violent storm, and a pigeon died. When Maximilien held the bird's rigid little body in his hands, he began to cry. These tears, which I wiped away, were the only ones he ever let me see.

For two years more we lived in close friendship, a friendship that was certainly deeper than our years might have suggested. *"Fidus achate"* the college regent often repeated as he placed his hand on my shoulder. The good man blessed the affection I had for his best scholar. I admit that my friend's success in his studies made me feel less mortified at being at the foot of the class. I was unconscious of envy, and thank heaven, I would rather have died than felt any. Maximilien's own talents were enough to make me proud.

But these very talents, recognized by everyone, were to be the cause of a long separation between us. One October evening in 1769 I said good-by to the sad and gentle orphan. Twelve years later I was to find a man so much more developed than I that he seemed almost a stranger.

During these years of growth—which seemed longer than all the rest of life—we lived apart. The thought occurs to me that if we had served our early apprenticeship in life side by side in our home town, Maximilien might have developed an entirely different character. For the provinces form a more moderate attitude toward things, and who knows if the progress of the Revolution and the future of France might not have taken an entirely different road, if Robespierre had grown up in Arras near the most obscure of his friends.

But these are useless regrets, superfluous conjectures. For Fate itself ruled things differently.

CHAPTER FIVE

THE success my friend had attained in the classes of our little school came at last to the ears of the Abbé of Saint-Waast. This all-powerful prelate interested himself in the future of the orphan, whose misfortunes had been told to him. Having sent for his grandfather, he offered in behalf of Maximilien one of the four scholarships to the College Louis le Grand the abbé had at his disposal. The old Carrault bowed to the floor with thanks, and then ran to pack up his grandson's belongings.

At the departure of the coach, he slipped a few pieces of gold into Maximilien's pocket. Maximilien climbed up on the roof of the coach. I stood by. I watched the brown coach-chest wind through the square and disappear along Rue Saint-Aubert, toward the gate of Amiens. Evening came. The coach agent closed the door of his office. Then old Carrault seemed suddenly to notice that I was still there. He cleared his throat self-consciously and after patting me on the shoulder, led me home to my family.

For two years I received no news from my friend. In town they said the young foundation scholar proved himself worthy of the hopes his patrons had placed in him. He passed his holidays with a relative, M. l'abbé de Laroche. In the vacations which followed, Maximilien returned to Arras. I saw him for scarcely more than a few moments. He seemed thoughtful, restless. He showed a deep tenderness for his brother and his younger sisters. He left his grandparents' house very seldom, and read a great deal. In the first week of September he returned to school.

Two or three more years passed. Already this friendship which had been so dear to my early years was beginning to wear away. I thought I was forgotten. Other friends were dividing the interests of my heart, when Fate, set implacably against Maximilien, dealt him a new blow. His favorite sister, Henriette, died of the same illness which had carried off her mother. She was fifteen.

Maximilien arrived as she was dying. At the painful moment when the coffin was being lowered into the grave, he saw me near him, and flung himself into my arms. My resentment, his ingratitude—all were forgotten. I had again found my friend, whom I pressed to my breast.

During those few days while he remained among us he showed me the same friendship as of old. However, it was then for the first time that I realized how different we really were. Already Maximilien revealed more character of will than natural endowments. He was a thoughtful child, but one who never dreamed. Studious, he searched for the cause and reason of all things. My enthusiasm and my carelessness astonished him, even as the excess of my sensitivity did. In his eyes they were only the signs of weakness and inferiority. He had returned to us loaded down with the scholastic honors of a too-bookish student.

His seventeen years already despised the enchantment of the imagination, as much as they despised the doubts of conscience. I will not delay in giving a proof of this.

I learned from him what life was like at school. He drew a picture for me of the somber corners and the sad walls of Louis-le-Grand. Finally he confessed to me that he had struck up a friendship with another young foundation scholar, whose name he told me. Overcome to learn that an unknown had supplanted me in his heart, I did not then hear the name. I heard only that my rival was the son of a Lieutenant-General in the county of Guise. My jealousy of this friendship was pleasing to Maximilien, although he made pretense to the contrary.

"Then you would only care for an unsociable friend?" he asked, with an accent of reproach. "I bear no hard feelings toward you. I will always find you agreeable, with all your faults, and even the excess of your feelings proves that your heart is truly generous. But never forget, my friend, that liberty is the most precious of all blessings. . . ."

Surprised at this remark, I stared at Maximilien. In spite of his young face, he had an indescribable air of maturity when he spoke. The old relation between us had returned. His life as a student in Paris was making a man of him, while I, two years younger than he, still remained an awkward and timid schoolboy.

The day before his departure I was invited to dine with his grandparents. After dinner Maxmilien wished to walk with me from the Rouville gate all the way to my home. I have forgotten nothing of this walk. We were then in early March, days that are usually chilly with us in Arras. The sky was clear, and round white clouds floated slowly over the belfries. We went along Rue de Rouville and Rue des Trois-Faucilles. Birds skimmed over the roofs of houses like arrows. As the "young Derobespierre" passed, the townspeople pointed him out to one another. He took no notice of this, but continued speaking in the same terse, dogmatic way he had spoken the day before.

Thus I learned that one of his teachers, the Abbé Hérivaux, held him in particular esteem, that he loved to talk with Maximilien during the hours of recess, that he was bringing him up in the love of antiquity and austere morals.

"He has nicknamed me the Roman," said Maximilien proudly, "and that is what everyone at school calls me now."

Then, changing the subject, he astonished me by his knowledge of Rousseau's works. Among us at that time he was discredited and scarcely known, this author Jean Jacques, for we provincial scholars had no means of forming a judgment on any of the contemporary writers. But Maximilien's assurance, his explanations of "Emile" or of the "Social Contract," filled me with admiration. He knew long passages by heart, and I observed then that the color of his words, that tone of preaching which had astonished me so much a few days before, were derived from the admired and beloved phraseology of the Genevese citizen.

Thus while I, in the quietness of our old city, had stayed a docile schoolboy, my friend had already chosen the master whose disciple he remained to the bitter end. So much knowledge, such precocious wisdom, confused me. Yet, nevertheless, admiring my friend's unique gallantry of manners and dress, I realized there was something in the air of Paris which existed nowhere else in France.

The next day I found myself alone. I soon learned from a letter sent by Maximilien that his teachers had chosen him from among all his fellow students to deliver the speech of welcome to the King, who, returning on the 11th of July, 1775, from his coronation at Reims, was to stop for a moment at the College Louis-le-Grand. I replied with a letter full of enthusiastic praise. A second letter came some little time later. Its tone was entirely different. I kept it for a long time, but an unfortunate accident finally deprived me of it. Perhaps some day a collector will come across this rare document, covered with that neat and fine handwriting which was so integral a part of Maximilien's character that it never varied. Moreover, I learned this letter almost by heart. After a few protestations of affection, he reproached me for the jealousy I had displayed. He told me that friendship is worthless if one submits to its precepts morosely and with a rueful face. He told me again that the friend against whom I had taken umbrage merited, on the contrary, all the marks of favor I formerly accorded himself.

Maximilien told me his name was Camille, and that he belonged to the same social class as I myself. His father was M. Desmoulins of Guise in Picardy, and was a petty official like my father.

One can imagine what I felt on receiving this letter. When Maximilien wrote it he was almost eighteen. I myself was a little less than sixteen. This terse and cutting criticism of friendship affected me like a message of farewell, and the praise of young Camille Desmoulins it contained was a sufficient hint to me that Maximilien had made his choice. For what was I, a poor country lad, compared to this happy partner of his ideas?

It was a singular thing that this letter caused me less anger than it did admiration. I found it superb and full of assurance. Did it not bring to me the first warning of those "new ideas" which had found an echo even in the most austere school of the kingdom? As a matter of fact, we were close enough to Paris for the effects of national events to find reëchoes in our own city. Two years previously, the description of the hideous funeral of Louis the Bien-Aimé had stirred the people of Artois as much as it had stirred the Parisians. Then terrifying words had been whispered about; bankruptcy was mentioned. Turgot came. He worked for the common people, amid the wrangling of grafters and favorites.

At the moment when I received the letter from Maximilien, Turgot was about to be turned out of office. We knew few things in Arras, but in the Parisian cafes they talked only of social questions and public interests. Was it astonishing then that the "new ideas" had finally penetrated the thick walls of the schools?

But to return; this letter which I considered as the occasion of rupture I refrained from showing not only to my parents but to Maximilien's brother and sisters as well. I had cause later to regret my susceptibility. Moreover I lacked leisure for reflection. My turn had come to leave Arras, for at last I was to enter the University of Douai.

Due to the facts I have just mentioned, I ceased to correspond with Maximilien. A student's life with all its pleasures soon quieted my sorrows. In three years I had taken my degree. Nevertheless, by the wise decision of my father, my stay in Douai was protracted by a rather long period of clerkship in the office of an attorney in the court of Flanders.

When I at last returned to my family, in April, 1782, I promptly heard that Maximilien also had returned. I was to see him that very day. He was wearing glasses. Leaning on his arm was his sister Charlotte. They were walking slowly along a little street toward the public square, which was flooded with sunshine.

CHAPTER SIX

HE was called M. de Robespierre the elder, and he took pleasure in emphasizing the *de* of his name.

The first time that we met face to face was in the salon of Mme. Foacier de Ruzé, wife of the Advocate General. She entertained with much graciousness. Pleasure as well as ambition led many young law students to her house, for under her paneled ceiling one could find the more eminent lawyers of the province.

Hardly had I entered the room when I saw Maximilien. I recognized him in a moment, even though the Maximilien I now saw was entirely different from the young schoolboy I had known before. Paris had returned us a smart young gentleman dressed almost to the point of foppishness. His clothes, however, revealed more signs of care than they did of cost. His face was oval, ending in a high broad forehead; his hair was brushed backward and waved. His lips were thin and gave to his face a coldly ironic expression that was rather unpleasant.

He wore a coat with a turned-up collar and large buttons; a satin vest; a pair of watch ribbons, with their charms, dangled against his breeches of black cloth. As he walked, he held a *chapeau de bras* against his side. His hair was carefully powdered. His powdered hair and a collar of snowy batiste were his sole affectations, luxuries he always refused to renounce. Nevertheless, he was not entirely at ease. His coat had been brushed too often. Under their silver buckles, his shoes were of too ecclesiastical a heaviness. Altogether this pale young man with the penetrating eyes had an air that was a bit too serious for his years. It was slightly too studied.

Upon seeing him I remained glued to the floor. He did not appear to notice my confusion, or rather he may have laid it to my excess of joy. His own pleasure seemed real. At any rate, upon seeing me he rose from the chair where he had been talking to a group of people who had gathered around him. He came toward me, holding out his hands, and at once led me into the recess of a window.

I was large and strong, five feet ten inches tall, of true Flemish build. My height filled my old school friend with astonishment, for to look into my face he had to tip back his head. In his expression there was both admiration and irony. Using the language of an age overfond of mythology, he complimented me:

"I left Ganymede and I return to Hercules."

"They speak well," I replied in the same tone, "who call you the rival of Amphion."

Laughing, at ease, we looked at each other. He spoke of our boyhood. A thousand memories illumined our past, which now seemed so distant to our twenty years.

From our hearts these thoughts rose to our lips. The faith we had in the future cast a new light on our words, and soon the events of our youth seemed no longer a confused and meaningless revery.

Maximilien had thrown himself whole-heartedly into a career that I was entering with less assurance. Arras, however, offered a most brilliant future to lawyers. The city at that time counted five ordinary jurisdictions: the *Gouvernance,* the municipal court, the Abbatical chamber of Saint-Waast, the Provost of the Diocese, the Temporal Court; and four Royal jurisdictions: the *Élection-Provinciale,* the Department of Streams and Forests, the Maréchausée, and the Superior Provincial Court of Artois. To plead before all these bailiffs, mayors, sheriffs, knights, provosts, lieutenants, judges extraordinary, attorneys general, under-bailiffs, under-provosts, etc., there were only eighty-two lawyers.

There were too few, and too many. Our elders, trained in the intrigues of the salon and court, passed all legal cases through a sieve, leaving only the little ones to their younger confrères. To reach success entailed a long and difficult journey, particularly for those who set forth with neither fortune nor influence.

But Maximilien flung himself courageously into the struggle. Against the attacks of men in power he felt himself well armed. His early misfortunes, as well as his humble position as foundation scholar, had accustomed him at an early age to count on no one save himself. In fact, through solitude he had acquired that profound restraint and that devouring ambition which, when fused with patience, creates the perfect ruler.

All this I felt only in terms of prophecy. To speak frankly, what struck me more, at the time, was the prestige over the minds of his young fellow lawyers his life in Paris gave him. I mentioned this fact to him. He smiled with an expression of conceit that was very displeasing to me. After all, he never learned how to conceal his pride. Pride was his great and perhaps his only weakness. Through it he was to lay himself open to his enemies. It was pride again that one day estranged me—I, who loved him well! And it was to bind up his wounded and beaten pride that I returned to him in his last hours. But it is not yet time for me to speak of it. . . .

Let us return to Mme. de Ruzé. This lady did not like conversations held apart from the company. She swept over to us and addressed herself to Maximilien.

"M. de Robespierre," said she, "no one can resist you. You run off with all my friends. But how can one blame you?"

"I know you are forgiving, Madame," he responded, bowing, "and if I were to refuse my thanks I would be unjust as well as ungrateful. But the young man here is my only boyhood friend. I have not seen him for five years."

"You will see more of him later, since, if what I hear is true, he is to be your confrère at the bar in Arras."

"You are not mistaken, Madame," said I in my turn. "But I would not dare to set myself up as a rival of Maximilien, whom Paris has returned to us, covered with laurels."

"Court-room flattery!" said he with a dry smile.

But at the same time he struck me affably upon the shoulder. Then he offered his arm to Mme. de Ruzé and we moved into the neighboring room, where the first chords of *"Triste apprêts, pâles flambeaux"* were being played and the President de Beaumetz was preparing to sing.

From that day, our friendship was renewed. The custom our fathers had maintained of returning from court together now became ours.[1]

Maximilien talked a great deal. By a faculty of mind common to most orators he developed his thoughts as he expressed them. An auditor was constantly necessary. He required someone who would lend himself completely to the rôle of disciple, whom he could instruct at will, and who would never interrupt him, even to applaud. This weakness, though innocent enough, after all explains many things in his life.

For the time being I was his auditor. Every day, a little after noon, while we returned home walking slowly arm in arm, Maximilien vouchsafed to me alone that eloquence which in so near a future was to make all France tremble. Our conversations, or, rather, to speak prop-

[1] I should here set the biographers right on a point in which nearly all of them go astray. They put Robespierre's birthplace in Rue des Rats-Porteurs, in a house which he rented many years later (about 1787) from a M. Dufetel. This house did not belong to Maximilien's family, who never owned any real estate.

At the time when he returned to Arras to practice his profession, he went to live with his sister at the house of his uncle, Dr. Durut, Rue des Teinturiers, behind the cathedral. It was to this house that I a great many times accompanied him from court.

erly, his orations, were devoted to social questions, to the natural order of things, the principle of laws, to the question of government, to the ideas of Raynal, Turgot, Grotius, Montesquieu—all of which he examined, revolved, picked apart, and sifted, to arrive finally at a eulogy of his own two gods, Mably and Rousseau.

His admiration for Jean Jacques had grown even more during his stay at Paris. Maximilien, then studying law at college, led the solitary, exalted, feverish life of a poor student. Often he wandered late through the outskirts of the city, under the yellow light of the street lamps which, hanging from their chains, pierced the night fogs.

Bitter solitude, which little by little became precious to him, shaped his character to virtue, when in his bare room he heard the silent and penetrating melody of the "Confessions" and the "Reveries." He learned "The Profession of Faith of the Savoyard Vicar" by heart, and never was able to recite in an unbroken voice that passage where his own sorrow and his own anguish seemed mirrored. "Although I have often met with greater pain, I have never led a life so constantly harrowing as in those times of trouble and anxiety, when ceaselessly wandering from doubt to doubt, I was led only to incertitude and obscurity by my long meditations—to contradictions on the cause of my existence and on the law of my conscience."

But Maximilien did not dare to compare his misfortunes to those numberless trials which brought the life of him whom he venerated to a close. So much distress would have overwhelmed his soul, so much ingratitude would have filled him with disgust. Rich at twenty years with his master's experience, Maximilien considered himself fully instructed in the lessons of life. He mixed little with his fellow beings, choosing rather to withdraw further and further from them. The austerity of his morals made him ridiculous; even his landlady found them amusing. But no matter. He lived outside the world, his eyes fixed inexorably upon his model.

CHAPTER SEVEN

"ROUSSEAU at that time," said Maximilien to me, "lived in a fifth floor flat on the Rue Plâtrière. My enthusiasm for him occasionally led me to the very door of his house. But pride held me there; I would not enter. I stationed myself at an angle in the street, and from there I saw entering and leaving M. Ducis, M. Bernadin de St. Pierre, M. Rulhière, the brave Dussaulx, and other famous writers, also ladies from the court and powdered gentlemen who lisped."

For a long time the young admirer of Rousseau, with his fixed, myopic eyes, observed all this. Then he would return to his home, vaguely jealous, but strengthened, full of the pure happiness of a lover whose timid hopes well up as he watches his lady's window. While he told this story of his past in a low and melancholy voice, he smiled to himself.

One evening about the middle of April, he extended his confidences further. Once more the scene appears before me. We were walking together through the gardens of the Esplanade. A gentle breeze passed like a long sigh through the trembling trees. Did the shadows and this light wind awake recollections of a similar evening? Or did this laughing tenderness of nature lure him into unlocking his heart to me? I do not know. He told me things which were no longer a secret between us. Some things he asked me never to tell, and I will not betray him. It was still on the subject of Rousseau.

First he told me that toward the end of May in the year 1778 he learned of a circular Jean Jacques had written and sent to a number of people. The terms of this letter had moved Maximilien profoundly. The great man begged for a place of refuge and bread for his old age, accepting in advance either forced seclusion or apparent liberty, a poor house or a desert, anywhere so long as his wife was also cared for and both of them should have food and shelter!

As soon as he had glanced through this letter which one of Rousseau's treacherous friends had published, Maximilien flew to Rousseau's home. Fie on discretion when distress had wrung so terrible a request from the divine Jean Jacques!

Maximilien arrived at Rue Plâtrière. In a breath he reached the philosopher's attic. Rousseau had gone. Three days before he had accepted the hospitality of the Marquis de Girardin at Ermenonville. Fortified with courage, Maximilien took the coach to Crépy-en-Valois and there inquired the way to the "Hermitage," where Rousseau had taken up his quarters.

Since that time I have often dreamed of this young man, his destiny charged with so great a future, taking his solitary way along the darkening road. . . . He was allowed to proceed to the philosopher's retreat. The light from a low window led him through the twilight. The door was closed. Maximilien knocked. There was no reply. He knocked a little louder. Then he heard a voice. Someone asked who was there. The young pilgrim felt himself grow pale, so moved that he clutched his breast with his hands. At last he was able to reply that he was a young man who asked the honor of seeing M. Rousseau. . . . The door opened. . . .

At this point Maximilien became silent. His eyes glanced toward the branches of a tree, stirred indolently by the breeze. And then, as if he spoke only for himself, he continued.

"He kept me in those heavy shadows of Ermenonville until midnight closed in upon us. . . . He was devoured with sadness. . . . He was the most sensitive of men, and yet those vile slanderers of his have made him out to be a monster. . . . My friend, listen to me! He stopped me in my first few compliments, telling me that flattery is only a coarse disguise through which peers the face of hate and treachery. He did not say that for me. It was for the false, and for hypocrites. But I have remembered the lesson. Soon afterwards he revealed himself in his own light of benevolence and frankness. . . . What more can I say about him? He taught me how to know myself. I was very young. He taught me to appreciate the dignity of my nature and to reflect upon the great principles underlying social order. . . . "

Again Maximilien became silent. I looked at him. In

his eyes I saw an astonishing exaltation. He, always so grave, so sealed, was transfigured!

"Ah, thou divine man!" he cried. "I have seen thee in thy last days. And the remembrance is for me the well-spring of joyful pride. I have contemplated thy venerable face, and I have seen the black marks of remorse the injustices of men have made there."

Maximilien rose from the garden bench on which we now sat. I followed him. In silence we wandered along the little river till we reached the barrack wharves. A full moon had risen, and like a cymbal of silver it climbed the skies. All the city, with its steeples and its arches, was the color of pearls. We walked side by side. Maximilien was in a deep revery. Vainly did I press him to complete his story. But finally he confided to me that Rousseau, old and near death, had failed him in none of his expectations, for to his young follower he had rendered the most precious of all gifts, a definition of virtue. . . .

As he said these words we reached Rue Teinturiers. Grasping my hand for a moment, Maximilien abruptly withdrew, opened the door of his house and disappeared.

It is easy to understand why the next day and the days following I abstained from asking him any questions. It was he himself who returned to his previous confidences, as we were returning together from an evening with Abbé Roman.

He told me first that Jean Jacques had shown both surprise and joy at discovering that so young a boy could understand his works so perfectly. This pleasure had encouraged his visitor. In the ancient park of Ermenonville, master and disciple had held a conversation that Maximilien always considered as the greatest event of his life. Later on he was to commemorate it. In April, 1794, on the eve of the Feast of the Supreme Being, Maximilien, alone, weary and thoughtful, was to return to the shadows of those same trees. In this pilgrimage he offered up his glory and that defeat he foresaw to the spirit of that man who was really to preside over the civic Pentecost. Under those trees he was to write his report of the 18th Floréal, which in his devout heart he dedicated to the apostle of civic religion, to the high priest of Nature. . . .

As to the words Rousseau had spoken to him, Maximilien kept them secret until death stopped his mouth. No one can find a trace of them in any of his papers. Once only did he break silence on this point, and it was to me. But in my turn I have promised to carry this secret to the tomb. I will not break my word.

CHAPTER EIGHT

SHALL I admit it? Something wounded the admiration I held for Maximilien and the confidence I had placed in him. In a word, I doubted his sincerity. Although during our conversations, he pretended to obey the doctrines of Rousseau to the very letter and seemed to identify despotism and royal authority, in the same general terms of execration, one heard him speaking a different language in public. If things must be called by their right names, I must in all sorrow confess that Maximilien spoke like a courtier.

One day in court he mentioned the Château de la Muette, a royal residence, and I was astounded to hear him praise the monarch, who, said he, had honored the château with his "august presence." He concluded his speech by calling upon "the sentiments of all France for a prince who was at once its delight and its glory." One other time while speaking of the *lettres de cachet* he cried, "What am I saying? Today they would still be something worse than a frightful memory, if the tutellary saint who watches over France had not placed on the throne a prince worthy of cherishing and protecting liberty. . . . Oh you, you whom a merciful heaven has granted us, Sire—I suppose it is not enough for us that you have checked the ravages of this plague during your whole reign!"

I did not know what to think of it. To my most pointed allusions, Maximilien made no reply. I went so far as to ask him directly, for it is not my nature to suppress my suspicions.

He halted and considered me for a long time without saying a word, with that piercing glance which was a mark of scorn. Then he shrugged his shoulders and we continued to walk on in silence. But I would not accept defeat.

"Maximilien," said I, "it is to you I owe my love of truth. *Vitam impendere vero.* Or wasn't that the motto of your master, Jean Jacques?"

"Oh, well," he replied with good humor, "is truth really so simple, so convenient as all that? Can't one hate despotism without insulting the prince? Is it within a king's power to say, 'I don't wish to be King of France?' Perhaps a day will come for our descendants, when the social contract will be respected by even those who are now its agents and representatives, when kings will learn that royalty is a social duty and not a mass of personal privileges. But it should not behoove a reasonable man to break with his own country. Let us be contented with a monarch who is a friend of the new order and one who still finds in his kingdom enough men of honor and energy to acknowledge and be worthy of him. . . . And after all, one must occasionally, in behalf of public interest, avoid the rigorous purity of abstractions."

I quote almost the exact words of Robespierre. They leave no doubt on one point. On the eve of the Revolution Maximilien was a Royalist. Some have lamented this, and I was the first among them to do so. I still reproach myself for it. But it should not be forgotten that even the most progressive men at this time were still loyal to the king. One could hardly count more than ten republicans in the whole realm. Still my great error was in counting Rousseau among them, he, whose "Confessions" expressed a deference and humility not only toward the King but toward the people of his court as well. Thus, where others were mistaken, I was mistaken, and Maximilien, as one has seen, sharply emphasized the mistake.

CHAPTER NINE

Is it necessary to say that in court we eagerly anticipated the first appearance of Maximilien, whose return to us had been heralded by a fame the general effect of which was as dangerous as it was flattering? Whoever was born and raised in the provinces can imagine what that day was like.

The graduate of the university of Paris pleaded his first case at the bar on the 27th of February, 1782, before a court room crowded with lawyers. The case (Marie-Anne de Bardoult vs. Marie-Anne Thelliez and associates: validity of a marriage contract) scarcely justified the eager curiosity it aroused. Maximilien appeared against an old court-room fox whose cunning easily achieved its purpose. Maximilien lost. This, as it was expected, scarcely surprised the audience, but the young lawyer disappointed them in another way. They expected some inexperience, as well as a certain difficulty in delivery. But everyone hoped to hear a voice full of that grace and clarity in which Paris would triumph. To their surprise, it was quite the contrary.

Maximilien spoke easily—too easily—but without eloquence. His manner was that of a cold preacher, his speech redundant and with an abuse of abstract words that verged on the ridiculous. Furthermore, the little lawyer seemed swollen with metaphysics under his toga. In brief, he was tiresome. The disaster was great. Slander and jealousy, which until this time had been kept within bounds, now ran untrammeled through the salons.

With his great pride, Maximilien naturally suffered from this failure, even more than he suffered later from the jeers and laughter of his fellow delegates in the Constituent Assembly. But proud and silent he asked no favors of popular opinion. He argued his cases with intense zeal. He proved himself honest, disinterested, and with slow obstinacy drove his career along that road in which others endowed with richer natural gifts, with more enthusiasm or higher birth, were to fail.

One case Maximilien handled made his name famous. It was an attempt to obtain a reversal of a burlesque decree rendered by the Échevinage de St. Omer, condemning some lightning rods a wealthy man named Vissery had placed on the roof of his house. His neighbor, an old maid, had been so frightened by their appearance that she had M. Vissery and his lightning rods prosecuted as a public nuisance.

This decree Maximilien appealed and won before the court of Artois. What an affair it was! Echoes of it are found in the *Mercure de France* itself, where the name of Robespierre was celebrated as lawyer and scholar. But the court-room audience, still numerous, held to its original opinion, finding the young lawyer's pleading as cold and dreary as it had been at first. I have before me now an imprint of the speech Maximilien had made.

"The Arts and the Sciences are the richest gifts Heaven has granted to mankind. Yet by what Fate have insuperable obstacles been placed between them and their establishment upon Earth? . . . Why cannot mankind render a just reward to scientists and inventors, a just reward of acknowledgment and admiration which humanity as a whole owes to them, without forcing them at the same time to groan over the shameful persecutions which render their discoveries as fatal to their repose as these discoveries are useful to the general welfare of Society?"

Such, at this time, was Maximilien's oratorical style. One of the lawyers at the bar in Arras, a certain Devienne who later became a prosecuting attorney, said of him, "M. de Robespierre has facility in speaking, but he is neither eloquent nor vigorous."

A thousand different estimations have since then confirmed the judgment of this unknown. His Royal Highness the Duke of Orleans, who in 1791 pleased to call himself "Citizen of Paris," and who never missed a meeting of the Jacobins, said not long ago at the *Chambre des Pairs* that "Robespierre was a bore in the supreme degree." I admit that this opinion springs from a tainted source. But it is also the opinion of others: Mirabeau, Barnave, La Fayette, all fall into agreement on the point that Maximilien lacked the true gift of eloquence.

I have often been questioned on this matter. Shall I, after so many illustrious critics, dare to express my own opinion? In behalf of truth I must. On Robespierre as an orator one can have, in reality, two judgments diametrically opposed. Until 1791 he had little reputation. His eloquence became evident to the Jacobins with his speech on the War, a speech that indeed still merits the admiration the most severe critics bestow upon it. From that moment, Robespierre became an outstanding figure on the tribune. By no means, as the envious declare, does he owe this sudden reputation to his friends. Devoid of all natural eloquence, he had schooled himself laboriously in his art. That he only achieved success very late in life, I admit. But is it not possible to find many illustrious precedents of slow and painful development? Did not Demosthenes practice for years with his pebbles? To speak the truth, the weakness Robespierre had to correct principally was neither his colorless voice nor his monotonous delivery. It was his verbosity. That drab facility which consists in the merciless repetition of the same figures, a flood of abstract expressions in which the central idea is drowned. He was, so to speak, incapable at first of expressing anything simply or neatly, of uttering those phrases, those epigrams, those compact and sublime retorts the greatest orators fling like medals stamped with their own likeness into the chasm of posterity. One need only to read the collection of his speeches at the Convention to realize that he learned eloquence at home. But it is necessary to admit that long and stubborn work alone enabled him to supply the gifts which nature had denied him.

It is also quite unjust to reproach him for reading his speeches at court. At that time it was a current practice in court, and only very rarely did anyone invoke the sacred frenzy of Calliope. As to the speeches, they were all modeled after the most strict academic style. Spontaneous eloquence was a child of the Revolution. In popular assemblies with their turbulence and sudden perils it was of course a necessity, but even at the Constituent Assembly Mirabeau alone dared speak extemporaneously. In the revolutionary assemblies the only two orators who spoke readily offhand were Danton and Vergniaud. Yet Danton finally dictated his speeches. Vergniaud alone most frequently trusted to his talent, and, as he said, let himself speak from his soul.

Later, the habit of speaking extemporaneously became slightly extended. But Maximilien never acceded to the custom unless pressed by the direst need. Later on for another reason, he did break into sudden and beautiful eloquence. But in general he read, and for this purpose he found two pairs of spectacles were necessary, one to read his speeches, the other to examine their effect upon his audience.[1]

People today find difficulty in believing this fact. They ask how, in the great days of the Convention, an orator less inclined to emotional than to rational appeal could prevail over so many flaming demagogues and fling them one after the other into the tumbrils to the guillotine. It was not the only miracle of his life.

[1] Bifocals were not invented until the time of Gladstone. *Tr.*

CHAPTER TEN

THE Rosatis met under an arbor of privet and acacia. It was into the company of these song-writers that Maximilien was one day elected. He comported himself there gallantly. According to the custom of our company, he thrice inhaled the fragrance of a rose. Then emptying a glass of *vin rosé* at a draught, he responded in verse to the usual compliments.

Later on he even composed and sang the following bacchic song:

Friends, with these speeches over fine
Let us have done, and drink some wine.
Who wouldn't get a little boozy
With Monsieur Cot and Monsieur Ruzé?
Whene'er old Carnot heaves in view
I think of wine, and cognac too.
So, friends, let's broach another keg.
Life is too short to plead or beg.

It was clumsy poetry, but this Maximilien knew, and knowing it, laughed. Carnot's rhymes were bad, too, but of all of them mine were the worst. My absurdity reached its height when I roared out my ariettes and bouquets to

Chloris with the voice of Stentor. Maximilien's voice was shrill and a little too sharp. We did not ask him to sing very often. The Rosatis, however, were for him only an antechamber to the Academy of Belles Lettres at Arras, into which organization he had an ambition to enter.

For each of us the name of Robespierre now evokes the idea of a Jacobin without weakness, with strict morals, vast ambitions, a generalizing mind, in fact a statesman entirely incapable of seeking after small honors, or of using his connections. Popular opinion is not wrong. But that man in reality existed only at Paris between June, 1789, and July, 1793.

Indeed one must try to imagine his mental attitude in 1782. Maximilien conducted himself like a man of his own social class. He was a young bourgeois who, preparing his career as provincial lawyer with persistence and zeal, neglected nothing which might favor his advancement. Above everything it was necessary for him to gain the esteem of his fellow-citizens, and particularly the judges and leading men of the city. The title of Academician of the Canton, which gives rise to laughter, overawed the salons of the austere provinces. Even today do we not see very honest people who are not complete fools striving after these imitated honors with an ardor and a tenacity not always displayed by candidates for the real ones?

Nevertheless, truth would be missing if the portrait of Robespierre at twenty-four should be painted in the simple colors of a provincial climber, entirely occupied in attaching himself to useful associates and in satisfying his social pride. An obscure inner debate disturbed him. In one way he felt himself far superior to the low intrigues of the bar that hemmed him round. I believe that he had always dreamed of dominating men, of occupying a place of great glory, of shining at the very top of the ladder.

On the other hand, these beautiful dreams were thwarted by his deep reverence for reason and prudence. He was far from being an enthusiast. Everything that was not obedient to his maturing plans seemed to him vain, deceitful, and without a future.

Confidence and doubt. Is it not in making a choice between these words that all young ambition is consumed? Thus did the young lawyer live, in admiration for vast schemes and in an aversion for hollow phantasies. If some flatterer had predicted a great destiny for him, he would have let his consuming pride break forth. But prudence would have soon quenched it. And Maximilien would fall back into his incertitudes.

He who does not know the old order of things scarcely can understand those struggles, those transports, those discouragements with which many a young man at that time was tormented. The Revolution not only equalized all classes, it favored young talent.

The author of this memoir has known this epoch, when life was not so sweet as M. Rivarol would have us believe. I can describe what a young man like Robespierre experienced during these years of expectancy. I see him in his legal robe, without wealth, almost without clients, with a brother and sister orphaned like himself—ceasing to struggle only when he dreamed.

He has all the appearance of tranquillity. He observes, he seeks, he feels his way awkwardly. Possessed as he is by the will to succeed, he is able only to project his hopes into a profoundly different world. Was he to attempt the impossible? He had too much common sense to exhaust himself in futile rebellions. He knows too well that through no expenditure of effort can he break through the walls of privilege. He measures his power and his abilities with the cool analytic mind of a lawyer. The nobility the *de* of his name implies, his coat of arms, two branches cantonned with four doves on a field of azure—he knows too well what they are worth. He knows his coat of arms came from a great uncle, collector of taxes at Épinoy, who bought them with good Artesian gold from the officials of the *Maitrise*. . . . Maximilien knows the value a sneering nobility places upon them. And his success in the University? Provincial envy is eager to belittle it, and, besides, is a Paris degree worth more than any other? Does a *Dilectissime matris Patronae* honor a man more for being pronounced on the banks of the Seine?

Maximilien knew himself. He was less hard-working than he was keen. He was quick to understand; he possessed that art, precious to all orators, of appropriating an idea to himself, or moulding it to his own purposes so cleverly that its author would applaud it himself without recognizing its source. But imagination he lacked, as he lacked also that ability for repartee and that nonchalance in delivery which captivates an audience. Speech-making taught it to him later. But at the start it was completely missing. Errors and miscalculations warned him that if he were to conquer, it would only be through obstinacy. And even what was boorish in his nature was to serve him later in that time when virtue dared to ignore pleasing manners.

Maximilien appraised himself coldly. But it did not prevent his evil genius from returning and assailing him. How could he tear down so many obstacles and achieve fame? How could he attain immortality? How could he raise himself above the mob? He carried concealed treasures in his heart, an entire system of politics, a profound knowledge of the weakness of his times, an absolute scorn of wealth, a deep belief in natural rights, a distrustful aversion toward the unjust and the complaisant, a patience that knows success does not come without a struggle, and finally, that fierce ardor of one who never surrenders to the domination of the mighty, that implacable rancor of the weak which strengthens David's arm and carries death to Goliath.

At that time, Danton the athlete, carrying off the daughter of a Parnassian café-owner in his arms, with a laughter that rattled the windows, scarcely suspected that his sentence of death was already written on the heart of a little priest-like lawyer in Arras, who denounced libertines in academic speeches.

But I, who now write about my friend and who see

his young face before me, know well that the true Robespierre whom I have loved was not the murderer of Danton. Robespierre at the summit of his work spent all to gain a popularity that was antagonistic to both his conscience and his soul. He was one of the elect. Fate, which made him powerful, made him lonely. Alas! Are not the hardest hearts the hearts of children? I loved him much, that Robespierre, obscure and proud in the streets of Arras. I loved, too, the reviled, misunderstood and disheartened Robespierre of Mesidor in the year II. He was the same man. But the Pontiff drunk with his idea of the Supreme Being, acclaimed by all the voices of a forgetful and capricious people—that merciless politician who broke Danton and Vergniaud—him I condemn. My consolation at the threshold of death is that my friend did not perish without knowing that I had always loved him for his true self, hating his false ideals and his cruel purpose.

CHAPTER ELEVEN

THESE early combats which took place in his conscience warmed his blood. Maximilien went on long walks. Under a large hat, he strode along the roads, replying carelessly to the salutations of the villagers. These walks became a habit with him. Only deep and quiet shadows would hold him back for a moment. One would see him sometimes seated under the elm of a churchyard. He would watch the little children play, remembering perhaps the pain of his own childhood, and then, with the same rapid and nervous stride, he would depart.

His more and more frequent disappearances astonished and disquieted his friends. What was there to do? They thought of finding him a wife. Possibilities were not lacking, but Maximilien would reply to all overtures only with a smile. Did he love women? What did love mean to him?

How many times have I been questioned on this subject! My silence has discouraged a thousand questioners. In truth the heart of Maximilien never yielded its secret. I do not believe that any woman in the world could say that she had held him at her mercy.

At the time we have reached in our story, he bothered

himself very little about them. But they? It is a lie that women hated him. How could they help but love him? The extreme care he took in his personal appearance was pleasing to them. But what touched them most were the marks of suffering on his face, the knowledge of his unhappy childhood, and the strictness of his morals. They knew the virtuous man is the most faithful lover, he who is most careful of his heart. More than one woman looked for a husband like him. Finally he became engaged. It was a shabby adventure, which is not worth repeating here.

Maximilien rambled along the roads after the manner of Jean Jacques. He never tired of this pleasure. In walking he made up verses to reply to the Rosatis. A certain M. Charamond had reproached him for his sobriety:

Friend Robespierre
Drinks water like Astruc.
Is he a cistern?
Is he an aqueduct?

And Maximilien replied:

O gods, I fear my pleasant friends
Will come to very arid ends.
The charming name, Rosati, may
Dry up, and wither quite away.
Blushing, I watch my friends and try
Hard to forget my throat is dry.

Our empty glasses standing there,
Like fishes with their mouths in air,
Should melt our hearts. O comrades mine,
Beware that god who first made wine.
Notorious water drinkers he
Will punish most relentlessly.
So drink! A glass of *vin rosé*
May quench his anger for a day.

At other times he composed less frivolous poems. Like his master Jean Jacques, nature inspired him, in the harmony of living things he found the unknown paths to human happiness. He reformed society while listening in woods to the singing of birds in old trees.

It was at the return from one of these excursions and just as he was removing his dusty shoes that his sister told him some now famous news. He leaped to his feet and hastened to the village square.

CHAPTER TWELVE

THE 9th of August, 1788, towards noon, a postilion, drawing up his horses before the groom at the coach station at Arras, cried:

"There's great news going the rounds in Paris!"

"What news?" asked the man in sabots.

"M. de Brienne has convoked the Estates."

The loungers who for lack of any other work waited near the station for the arrival of the coach hurried to spread the news they had just heard. Soon it was flying from door to door. In every corner of the city you heard only the words:

"The Estates. The Estates. The King convokes the Estates."

I met Robespierre on Rue du Conseil. He was mingling with the mob, as I was too, as was everyone in the city. He seemed strikingly pale. We walked a little distance together. He took my arm and said to me earnestly:

"Rousseau has said it. 'We are approaching a condition of crisis and a century of revolutions.'"

Then he withdrew and entered his house. During those great days which brought men out into the gathering places, he shut himself up in his room and went feverishly to work. It was a trait of his character, which Maximilien never abandoned. A man of the study, an invisible commander, only once did he mingle with the somber flood in the streets when tumult roared.

That was on his last night. . . .

So, after the words I have quoted, he left me to shut himself up in his room. One o'clock had just struck. Nor did he leave that day nor on the day that followed to take his customary stroll in the gardens of the Abbey. I remember that returning to my home late at night, I saw his shadow on the curtains of his window. He was writing.

It was an address to his fellow citizens, a discharge of grievances and hopes, enough to send a man to the Bastille for the rest of his days. . . . While Maximilien read this writing to me, before placing it in the hands of a printer, I remained speechless.

The title was: "An Appeal to the Artesian People, on the Necessity of Reforming the Estates of Artois, and on the Means of Arriving at that End." Maximilien examined the constitution of the Estates and its vices, tracing it to 1640, the time of the reunion of Artois and France. He wrote with accuracy of the taxes, of the salt tax, of the circulation of merchandise, of a frigate rigged at the expense of the province, of a dowry the Artesian people had collected for the daughter of the Duke of Levis, of the prebends. He recalled the edicts of Philip II. Then he passed on to Statute-labor, and the hauling of charcoal. After this he came to his conclusion. It was inflammatory. It contained passages in which the author even went so far as saying: "Since all the enemies of the people have audacity enough to make sport of humanity, should I lack the courage to reclaim its rights? In that moment when, after so many centuries, the voice of truth can energetically make itself heard; in that moment when vice, armed with unrighteous power, learns to tremble before justice and triumphant reason, should I keep a cowardly silence?"

In reading this, Maximilien lowered the manuscript of his appeal to emphasize its cadences and its falls. It was an oratorical gesture that was habitual with him. He observed the effects of his periods, on my face. I was overwhelmed. He noticed my reaction and smiled with pride. Finally he came to the apostrophe whose fire and passion would, in his estimation, arouse most anger and astonishment. "The moment has come when the sparks of sacred fire will enflame all life with courage and with happiness."

He rose and rubbed his hands together. At this moment his lean and nervous body, his cat-like face, as his followers in Arras described it, the pale light of his eyes, in fact his entire appearance, so ill-created for domination, seemed enveloped in a most unforeseen and singular strength. Such is the power of a steadfast mind. In that momentary flash, which passed and disappeared, I saw for a second all that the future held in promise for the little lawyer of Arras.

We went out. Already the streets had sunk into their somnolence and their solitude. We hastened to the printer. At the very idea of setting the appeal in type, the printer let the manuscript fall from his hands. Finally we found one who showed more backbone.

"You are a good citizen," Maximilien said to him.

The brochure made as much noise as one could have anticipated. I trembled for my friend. But already the terror of the *lettres de cachet* had passed. Versailles had developed more important troubles. M. de Brienne, when the national bonds fell due, was driven to pillage hospital funds and poor boxes. Even Necker had to be recalled.

"The other Genevese!" said Maximilien.

Finally, as a climax, came the terrible winter of '88, which the Artesians still call the Famine Winter. In the spring following, pamphlets sprang up all over France, each one in the same tone as that which Maximilien had written. He, meanwhile, had prepared another pamphlet, which appeared in March, 1789. This time it was to present himself as a candidate for the Estates General, amid a furious clamor which the nobles, clericals, judges, the garrison, and old marriage brokers raised from every corner of the city.

He ended his manifesto thus: "The Supreme Being will hear my prayers; He understands their fervor and their sincerity, and I have reason to hope that He will grant them."

God did grant them. The career of Maximilien Robespierre as a statesman began on the 17th of March, 1789.

That day the mayor and aldermen of Arras proclaimed to the sound of trumpets "in Breteque as well as on all cross roads of the city, town, outskirts and suburbs" that all inhabitants composing the third estate were, on Monday the 23rd, at seven in the morning, to assemble in the chapel of the college to elect delegates. The corporations were to gather apart in the rooms of their brotherhoods. Lawyers, goldsmiths, hatters, carpenters, merchants, wheat measurers, street porters, slaters, hack drivers, tavern keepers, linendrapers, grocers, solicitors, apothecaries, wig makers, plasterers, harness makers, billings, gunsmiths, school teachers, turners, coppersmiths, cutlers, dealers in old clothes or second hand dealers, chirurgiens, doctors, joiners, curriers, coopers, furriers, bakers, wood gaugers, tailors, shoemakers, miners, butchers, barrow men and fishmongers were to meet in the churches.

The other meeting, which Maximilien attended, was interrupted with yells and whistling. The same thing happened on the 27th, 28th and 29th of March, when it was necessary to draw up the general list of grievances. The next day the preliminary meeting of all the deputies of the Third Estate took place. On this occasion Maximilien published his "Advice to the Dwellers in the Country," which had an overwhelming success. On the 20th of April, the three orders met together in the nave of the Cathedral, before the people and in the presence of the Duke de Guênes. The mass of the Holy Ghost was celebrated. Finally on the 24th of April an assembly of the Third Estate took place in the general hospital. Its business was to elect eight delegates to the Estates General of the Realm, who were to go to Versailles at once.

Four days were found necessary to do this. As each name was announced it was applauded. Here they are, in the order in which they came: Payen, Brassart, Fleury, Vaillant, Derobespierre, Petit, Boucher, Dubuisson. The list included four farmers, two lawyers, a judge, and a merchant.

CHAPTER THIRTEEN

On the evening of the third of May, two young men followed by a porter left the house on Rue des Rats-Porteurs. A woman in black, after a lingering farewell to the smaller of these two men, responded ceremoniously to the salutation of the other, and then reëntered the house. The trunk the porter carried was light. He dragged it over to the coach office without much trouble. Six travelers, wrapped closely in their cloaks, were waiting there already, surrounded by women and children. They pulled off their hats. Maximilien responded with cold dignity. They were the other representatives of the province, ruddy faced and excited, peasants who were embarrassed by their hands and who stared at their luggage spread out in the street. The postillions arrived. They all began to embrace one another.

At the moment when the postillions began to strap down the top, my friend took his seat way back in the coach. I wiped my eyes as I closed the coach door. A groom came and raised the coach step. The crowd of curious still lingered. Already Maximilien had drawn a sheaf of paper and a pencil from his portfolio. The old coach lurched forward. I raised my hat. Others were waving their handkerchiefs. Behind the dim panes of the coach window I saw a grave smile, a powdered head which nodded a sign of farewell. Then the coach turned the corner.

Thus did M. de Robespierre the elder, deputy from Artois to the Estates General, depart from Arras. He was three days less than thirty-one years old.

CHAPTER FOURTEEN

A DOZEN or so letters, brought every now and then by the Paris coach, a few lines in the newspapers, that was about all that I heard of my friend for two long years. Later on, like everyone else, I learned more about his work in the first days of the Revolution. Nothing, certainly, would keep me from writing about it today, if I wished to be a historian. But we have had enough of such writing.

At Versailles he at first lived at the Sign of the Fox on Rue Sainte-Élizabeth. Later he rented a house in common with three colleagues, on Rue de l'Étang. I knew these three delegates. They were all good farmers, Celestin Fleury of Coupevielle, Charles-Marie Payen of Boiry-Becquerelle, and Augustin Petit of Magnicourt-sur-Canche. They swore only by Maximilien, lived in his shadow, and, all entangled in law making, ill at ease among the groves of Lenôtre, they already were homesick for their fields of barley and their hop vines.

It is well known that in the Estates General Maximilien remained entirely obscure, and that, if he played any rôle at all in the great events of that time, he was lost in the crowd of clerical delegates.

He took the Tennis Court oath, he escorted the King's

coach when it drove to Paris between a double file of delegates, he hoisted the cockade, he visited the Bastille, he examined the bust of Necker, he expressed an opinion on his most well-known colleagues, his future rivals. Malouet he declared was steeped in artifice, Target he found pompous, and Mirabeau he considered *nil* because the latter's moral character deprived him of all trustworthiness.

A little afterwards, on the 9th of November, 1789, I received a note from Maximilien. I learned that he was living in Paris in the quartier du Marais, 30 Rue Saintonge, in the house of a Mr. Humbert. He shared his room with a young man named Pierre Villiers, who later on became a captain of dragoons and who, I understand, is now an actor in comic opera.

In the first days of the National Assembly, Maximilien was extremely poor. So poor, indeed, that at the death of Benjamin Franklin, when the Assembly went into mourning, he had to borrow dark clothes from a man much taller than he. M. Pierre Villiers acted as his secretary and the two of them ate alone in a restaurant. Maximilien kept a mistress, a humble and pretty creature, twenty-five years old, who doubtless asked no greater pleasure than to render him a thousand little services. But he who knows Robespierre can realize how repugnant this sort of intimacy must have been to him. He gave the girl a quarter of his deputy's salary, and sent a half of the rest to his sister Charlotte, who still lived in the house in Arras.

Shall I speak here of Robespierre's real entrance into politics, which took place about this time? A hundred historians have done it already. Nearly all agree on this point, that Robespierre was a very assiduous representative at the Constituent Assembly, and that he spoke from the tribune as often as possible. He was continually jeered at for his manners, his accent and that provincial twist in his speech, which he overcame only after great trouble.

But let them laugh! Scorning his detractors, wearing them out by the sheer force of his obstinacy, mastering them by the diversity of his interests, he spoke on every subject. On taxes, insurrections, Jews, Corsica, vagrancy, on the clergy, extradition, the army, the colonies, legislative works, on the organization of the judiciary, the diplomatic committee, registry of lottery stewards, the grain traffic, the liberty of the press, *lettres de cachet*, on religious pensions for priests, on the right of carrying arms, the right of the chase, on the sparrows of Catullus, on the marriage of priests. . . .

It is pretended that he spoke less to impress himself upon the Assembly than for practice. That he was scarcely listened to. That he was found tiresome, lacking in both voice and warmth. That between Mirabeau and Barnave he was like a rusty weathercock squeaking in wind and thunder. That, according to Duport's jibe, he took the tribune to be a professorship of common law. That Le Chapelier, Lameth, Petion, Sieyes, eclipsed him. And finally that he hardly succeeded in doing more than to make the voluptuous and sophisticated audience of the Constituent Assembly laugh well and long.

What is certain is that in the midst of this thunder and singing he alone, quietly and persistently, outlined a doctrine—and a doctrine is of little service to an orator. In derision and envy he was nicknamed the "Candle of Arras." I very well remember this soubriquet which the Feuillants and their friends repeated everywhere with much relish.

This nickname, and others like it, enraged him. Maximilien rarely understood pleasantries. Even when young he never could tolerate them. He was, as someone said, born old. And moreover he was never master of the quick retort. I remember that at the bar at Arras a sudden sally of wit would disconcert him. To sum up, he was quick only in retiring within himself, of entering the shadowy ego of his mind, and this doubtless did him much harm, particularly in an assembly where wit often overrode wisdom.

At this time, who dared to prophesy the immense rôle Robespierre was to play in the Revolution? In the whole world was there a single man who had faith in the political future of M. Robespierre?

There was. But one only. Himself.

He believed in his star of destiny, and he foresaw everything: his glory, his power, and even his tragic downfall. He wrote as much to me on the 12th of June, 1791, in a letter that I learned by heart:

"I am called to a stormy destiny. I must follow my

DÉCLARATION

DES DROITS DE L'HOMME ET DU CITOYEN.

Le peuple François convaincu, que l'oubli et le mépris des droits naturels de l'homme, sont les seules causes des malheurs du monde, a résolu d'exposer dans une déclaration solemnelle ces droits sacrés et inaliénables afin que tous les citoyens pouvant comparer sans cesse les actes du gouvernement avec le but de toute institution sociale, ne se laissent jamais opprimer et avilir par la tyrannie, afin que le peuple ait toujours devant les yeux les bases de sa liberté et de son bonheur, le magistrat la regle de ses devoirs, le legislateur, l'objet de sa mission.

En conséquence, il proclame, en présence de l'Etre suprême, la déclaration suivante des droits de l'homme et du citoyen.

ARTICLE PREMIER

Le but de la société est le bonheur commun. Le gouvernement est institué pour garantir à l'homme la jouissance de ses droits naturels et imprescriptibles.

2.e Ces droits, sont l'égalité, la liberté, la sureté, la propriété.

3.e Tous les hommes sont egaux par la nature et devant la loi.

4.e La loi est l'expression libre et solemnelle de la volonté générale; elle est la même pour tous, soit qu'elle protége soit qu'elle punisse; elle ne peut ordonner que ce qui est juste et utile à la société, elle ne peut défendre que ce qui est nuisible.

5.e Tous les citoyens sont également admissibles aux emplois publics. Les peuples libres ne connoissent d'autres motifs de préférence dans leurs élections que les vertus et les talens.

6.e La liberté est le pouvoir qui appartient à l'homme de faire tout ce qui ne nuit pas aux droits d'autrui; elle a pour principe, la nature, pour regle la justice, pour sauve-garde la loi; sa limite morale est dans cette maxime, *ne fais pas à un autre ce que tu ne veux pas qu'il te soit fait.*

7.e Le droit de manifester sa pensée et ses opinions, soit par la voie de la presse, soit de toute autre maniere, le droit de s'assembler paisiblement, le libre exercice des cultes, ne peuvent être interdits.

La necessité d'énoncer ses droits, suppose ou la présence ou le souvenir récent du despotisme.

8.e La sureté consiste dans la protection accordée par la société à chacun de ses membres pour la conservation de sa personne, de ses droits et de ses propriétés.

9.e La loi doit protéger la liberté publique et individuelle contre l'oppression de ceux qui gouvernent.

10.e Nul ne doit être accusé, arrêté, ni détenu que dans les cas déterminés par la loi et selon les formes qu'elle a prescrites.

Tout citoyen appelé ou saisi par l'autorité de la loi doit obéir à l'instant; il se rend coupable par la résistance.

11.e Tout acte exercé contre un homme hors des cas et sans les formes que la loi détermine, est arbitraire et tyrannique; celui contre lequel on voudroit l'exécuter par la violence, a le droit de le repousser par la force.

12.e Ceux qui solliciteroient, expédieroient, signeroient, exécuteroient ou feroient exécuter des actes arbitraires sont coupables, et doivent être punis.

13.e Tout homme étant présumé innocent jusqu'à ce qu'il ait été déclaré coupable, s'il est jugé indispensable de l'arrêter, toute rigueur qui ne seroit pas nécessaire pour s'assurer de sa personne, doit être sévèrement reprimée par la loi.

14.e Nul ne doit être jugé et puni qu'après avoir été entendu ou légalement appelé, et qu'en vertu d'une loi promulguée antérieurement au délit. La loi qui puniroit des délits commis avant qu'elle existât, seroit une tyrannie; l'effet rétroactif donné à la loi seroit un crime.

15.e La loi ne doit décerner que des peines strictement et évidemment nécessaires; les peines doivent être proportionnées au délit et utiles à la société.

16.e Le droit de propriété est celui qui appartient à tout citoyen de jouir et de disposer à son gré de ses biens et de ses revenus, du fruit de son travail et de son industrie.

17.e Nul genre de travail, de culture, de commerce, ne peut être interdit à l'industrie des citoyens.

ART DIX-HUITIEME

Tout homme peut engager ses services, son temps; mais il ne peut se vendre, ni être vendu: sa personne n'est pas une propriété aliénable. La loi ne connoît pas de domesticité; il ne peut exister qu'un engagement de soins et de reconnaissance, entre l'homme qui travaille et celui qui l'emploie.

19.e Nul ne peut être privé de la moindre portion de sa propriété sans son consentement, si ce n'est lorsque la nécessité publique légalement constatée l'exige, et sous la condition d'une juste et préalable indemnité.

20.e Nulle contribution ne peut être établie que pour l'utilité générale. Tous les citoyens ont droit de concourir à l'établissement des contributions, d'en surveiller l'emploi, et de s'en faire rendre compte.

21.e Les secours publics sont une dette sacrée. La société doit la subsistance aux citoyens malheureux, soit en leur procurant du travail, soit en assurant les moyens d'exister à ceux qui sont hors d'état de travailler.

22.e L'instruction est le besoin de tous. La société doit favoriser de tout son pouvoir les progrès de la raison publique, et mettre l'instruction à la portée de tous les citoyens.

23.e La garantie sociale consiste dans l'action de tous, pour assurer à chacun la jouissance et la conservation de ses droits; cette garantie repose sur la souveraineté nationale.

24.e Elle ne peut exister si les limites des fonctions publiques ne sont pas clairement déterminées par la loi, et si la responsabilité de tous les fonctionnaires n'est pas assurée.

25.e La souveraineté réside dans le peuple; elle est une et indivisible, imprescriptible et inaliénable.

26.e Aucune portion du peuple ne peut exercer la puissance du peuple entier; mais chaque section du souverain assemblée, doit jouir du droit d'exprimer sa volonté avec une entière liberté.

27.e Que tout individu qui usurperoit la souveraineté, soit à l'instant mis à mort par les hommes libres.

28.e Un peuple a toujours le droit de revoir, de réformer et de changer sa constitution. Une génération ne peut assujettir à ses loix les générations futures.

29.e Chaque citoyen a un droit égal de concourir à la formation de la loi, et à la nomination de ses mandataires ou de ses agens.

30.e Les fonctions publiques sont essentiellement temporaires; elles ne peuvent être considérées comme des distinctions ni comme des récompenses, mais comme des devoirs.

31.e Les délits des mandataires du peuple et de ses agens ne doivent jamais être impunis. Nul n'a le droit de se prétendre plus inviolable que les autres citoyens.

32.e Le droit de présenter des pétitions aux dépositaires de l'autorité publique ne peut, en aucun cas, être interdit, suspendu, ni limité.

33.e La résistance à l'oppression est la conséquence des autres droits de l'homme.

34.e Il y a oppression contre le corps social, lorsqu'un seul de ses membres est opprimé; il y a oppression contre chaque membre lorsque le corps social est opprimé.

35.e Quand le gouvernement viole les droits du peuple, l'insurrection est pour le peuple, et pour chaque portion du peuple, le plus sacré et le plus indispensable des devoirs.

DECLARATION OF THE RIGHTS OF MAN.

Displayed throughout France during the Revolution.

road until I have made the supreme sacrifice that I am able to offer to my country."

This letter, written eight days after the flight of Louis XVI, seems prophetic now. But these sentences would have made many who considered themselves the wisest judges in the world merely shrug their shoulders. Ah, if by chance or by plot the wits of the *Manège* had had these lines before them, what jokes, what mockeries there would have been!

Indeed they were easily amused, when it concerned my friend. With what complaisance did they repeat and mouth again the jibes of Mirabeau. "This poor lousy wretch is not to be feared on the tribune, but it would be dangerous if you sat beside him to drink." Or this one: "M. Robespierre is a cat who drinks too much vinegar." A cat! The little masters of the Salon Lameth screamed with laughter.

They laughed. But meanwhile they began to hear the little orator, with his shrill voice, this pale, short-sighted preacher who "believed everything he said." Suddenly they will judge his stature better. One fine day they will surrender everything to him. At his command they will vote their own political death.

When discussion occurred as to whether the delegates of the Constituent Assembly were eligible for reëlection to the next assembly, Thouret's report, loudly applauded, concluded with: "The members of the present legislature ought to be allowed reëlection." Robespierre climbed to the tribune and spoke as follows: "The greatest legislative bodies of antiquity, after having given a constitution to their country, considered it a duty to return to the mass of common people and to strip themselves of all public reward."

The assembly heard this. They soon knew what he meant. In brief, straightforward words, he said to them: "Come, let us go. Let us go now to our departments and find out what they think there of the Revolution. Let us breathe the air of that equality we have made. Let us leave this place to others. Let us enjoy a rest both nature and reason command."

It was an adroit move, played by the most skilful of politicians. For here the Clubs expressed themselves in the mouth of an orator who, in dispersing the Constituent Assembly, hewed down his rivals. Would he disappear with them? Without doubt. But Robespierre, the leader of the Jacobins, controlled the Jacobins. And the Jacobins controlled the workers, and the workers were going to control Paris and all of France.

CHAPTER FIFTEEN

MEANWHILE wagons, coaches and berlines choked the Artesian post roads. Through Arras, where I still remained, streamed every kind of vehicle packed with fleeing nobles, their servants and their strong boxes. Over the rough roads they struggled toward Austrian Flanders and the Low Countries, bribing their guides, fighting their way through bogs and mud, forcing their wheel horses and driving their leaders till they fell. Even the capture of Louis in his flight toward the border did not diminish the ardor of these emigrés, nor the zeal with which the coach owners enriched themselves. It should be added that to the provinces the spectacle of these wealthy fugitives hastening from the country was a more impressive proof of the advancing revolution than all the fine speeches of the delegates. It was even more impressive than Robespierre's famous speech on the *"Marc d'argent"* [1] which the *Club des Cordeliers* had printed and circulated throughout the country.

In the Assembly, where eloquence soared to extol liberty and fraternity, Robespierre alone remained the

[1] The *"marc d'argent"* was a property tax, equivalent to three days' labor. It was the minimum tax required to obtain franchise. *Tr.*

apostle of equal suffrage. Thus did he build his destiny upon the people, or to speak more accurately, upon the Clubs. Little by little, hereafter, his career unfolded in the form predicted by Barnave. The electors in resorting to the ballot had delivered the power of the law to the new deputies. Yes, but honor they tendered to Robespierre. In full support of him he had the poor, the slaves, the "passive citizens," all those who, in default of paying their *"marc d'argent,"* found their only political recourse in insurrection. And Robespierre realized that the Legislature, a mere assembly of novices, would remain a powerless debating society if the Clubs, like great seething vats, decided to brew the work of the revolution themselves.

CHAPTER SIXTEEN

I MUST again speak of myself. It was at this period that I received news of Tiburce for the first time. Twenty-six years had passed since he had quit home. It was said that he had dragged out a miserable existence in every country, that those in power had entrusted him with secret missions, that he had been seen at London, Amsterdam, Venice, that finally, after a sojourn in the dungeon of Vincennes, he had succeeded in getting a position as a solicitor's clerk in the old Rue du Temple. I have never been able to separate truth from fiction in these tales.

What I know is that during the first months of the Revolution Tiburce was at Paris, his nose to the wind. Like so many other adventurers, he frequented the Clubs and could be seen, in the blue uniform of the National Guard, standing sentinel before the Club Breton in the Place des Victoires. At the same time he opened an office for the settlement of disputed claims in the quarter of Arcis. He was then approaching his fiftieth year. Later he became a member of the civil committee in his section, one of the most desperate in Paris, but supported himself meanwhile by copying out reports for the administration.

It was this employment which, one day in June, led

him to the Tuileries. As he wandered through the maze of corridors, he happened to run into a citizen of provincial appearance who seemed to be about his own age. The two recognized each other. The stranger was a lawyer from Arras, who had been Tiburce's school fellow at college. Tiburce, embarrassed and ashamed, tried to slip away, but the lawyer in question, a friendly and pleasant fellow, seemed so genuinely happy at meeting him that the two left the court together. Now this lawyer was not only a friend of mine but a particular friend of Maximilien, whose admittance to the bar he had greatly facilitated. He took Tiburce so well in hand that he persuaded him to renew relations with his family, or rather with me, for both our parents had died. My brother therefore wrote me at Arras; I replied. From that day we kept up a more or less regular correspondence. Tiburce manifested a great desire to "press to his heart his younger brother, whom he had not seen since he was a child," and "he was living in hope that the day was near which would see us tenderly united."

Meanwhile he was pushing his way to the front. Like all men of his character, having gone through every kind of adventure, he had learned to handle himself with cunning and prudence. He was at all times clever enough to ask no favors, neither rank nor position, restricting all evidences of his patriotism to clearing up the difficulties of his clients.

As for me, I continued my profession in the province. Time hung heavy on my hands. With mild curiosity I looked forward to meeting this tormented ghost, my brother, whom the miracle of the Revolution had suddenly cast up from the other world, and who was now busily preparing to make a fortune for himself.

CHAPTER SEVENTEEN

DID I in reality support myself by my profession? What I have just said about it was perhaps dictated by my vanity. To speak frankly, I vegetated. A lawyer without clients, as he was without talent and ambition, careless of expense and extravagance, I gradually saw my inheritance melt away. It hardly existed. Nevertheless I maintained my position as a sturdy provincial. Bachelor and good liver, I dined out; I frequented the salons of Arras. As I had abstained from all political activity, even though I concealed neither my sympathy for the new order nor my friendship for Maximilien I was received everywhere and everyone, without exception, spoke freely before me.

What did they think of Maximilien in his native city? How did society in Arras consider the orphan, the scholar, the little lawyer of Rue Rats-Porteurs, who, as fifth delegate from Artois to the Estates General had so quickly eclipsed his colleagues and become famous?

One can imagine what the aristocracy of lawyers said. The province then, just as it is today, was envious and full of backbiting. Never did it praise his work. To the provincials, Paris, in raising one of their citizens to the

one protested, pretending to choke with the idea. Then another lawyer, Dr. Devienne, took the floor.

"Imagine him playing at jurisprudence! Isn't that shameful? He doesn't know any more about legal procedure than a clerk's cook. And when I think he was even forced to beg me to draw up his conclusions for him!"

"It appears," said another, "that everyone calls him 'Mirabeau's lap dog.'"

More laughter. But M. Devienne continued.

"An ex-member of the Rosatis, one of our friends, has made up some rather cutting verses on M. de Robespierre. Let me repeat them:

'This Robespierre who descends from Damiens
Takes after his father and is only an arrant rogue.
To the galleys with him!
He'd pull an oar right well.'"

These verses, as well as this talk, I found altogether flat, and I said as much. I can still see the expression of astonishment on their faces. What did they think of the man whose friend they continually slandered? They let me understand that my excess of loyalty to Maximilien hurt me very much in the estimation of all decent people. I broke into laughter, and one evening while dining at Rue Rats-Porteurs, I jested about the scene to Charlotte and to Robespierre's brother.[1]

[1] Robespierre the younger, since 1789, had been my confrère at the bar. He had taken his brother's place in the dormitories of College

The scorn with which the envious wasted their time amused Augustin and me very much. Charlotte did not laugh with us. Her disposition was not playful. In this she resembled her elder brother Maximilien more than the easy-going Augustin, and she suffered from the hostility of the town. She burned to join Maximilien, to drop her rôle of idle bourgeoise and to accept some sort of work.

"Maximilien at least ought to find some post in Paris for Augustin. Shouldn't he? You will never get anywhere in this place, my poor Bonbon!"

"Upon my word, that's true enough," responded Robespierre the younger. And he laughed.

As for me, the society of Arras honored me with a plot. From this time, I found myself exposed to a thousand annoyances. There was nothing my associates at the bar would not stoop to. Some months earlier various positions which would have assured my independence had been offered me.

Until the month of October, 1891, life became more and more difficult for me. But my private trouble is not the theme of this book.

Louis-le-Grand; during the holidays of 1788 he returned to Arras. At his return he had installed himself with his sister in the house on Rue Rats-Porteurs. He afterwards left for Paris. But in March, 1791, he returned and was appointed to the Council of Administration of the Department. Then the People's Society of the Trois-Faucilles, the Friends of the Constitution, chose him for their president. His given names were Augustin Bon. His sister and his friends called him "Bonbon." In the city he was given another nickname, "The Dauphin," and he was the first to laugh at it. He was a well-made boy, intrepid, noisy, vain, quite narrow, who would have made an excellent army man. He idolized Maximilien and everyone who was attached to him.

CHAPTER EIGHTEEN

At Paris, Maximilien dominated the closing days of the Assembly.

About this time there was an exhibition of paintings. On view were the "Horaces" of David, the sketches for the "Tennis Court Oath," the "Pasiello" of Mme. Vigee-Lebrun, the "Latude" by Vertier. And in one room, thronged with the fashionable and buyers from the Palais Royal, hung a pastel by Mme. Labille-Guyard. It was picture 84. The portrait was that of Maximilien Robespierre, dressed in a small cloak and an organdie shirt. Everyone recognized him, although the only indication the picture bore was a little gilt plaque attached to the frame, on which the visitors to the gallery read:

THE INCORRUPTIBLE

CHAPTER NINETEEN

GRIM news spread throughout the land. On Sunday the 17th of July, many thousands of citizens, dressed for the holiday, went to the Champs de Mars where, on the altar of the Fatherland they were to sign a petition to the Assembly against its recent vindication of the King. They were massacred. After a deadly volley had strewn the ground with corpses, the cavalry charged and sabred what was left of the crowd. When the massacre was over not a single weapon was found lying on the grass, not a single dead man with powder-blackened hands. The butchered populace were only holiday makers, children, couples, old people, down to peddlers of licorice-water and Nanterre cakes.

After this valiant piece of work, the guards marched back along Rue Royale. These troops, interspersed with bourgeois in blue coats, no longer knew any restraint. Brandishing their rifles, they threatened to exterminate all brigands. What brigands? Certainly not the ring-leaders of that group who had fired on La Fayette and wounded his aide-de-camp. To these deluded men, the brigands were the friends of the people, the deputies of anti-monarchist leanings, the writers of petitions, the democratic journalists, the leading patriots, the Club orators.

The guards, growing more and more excited, debouched from Rue Saint Honoré near Place Vendome, into that section where the various popular societies held their meetings. Their threats became more violent. At the triple gate of the Jacobins the rioters found the iron grilles shut. The Jacobins were meeting. A mob representing both sides choked up all the approaches, all the way to Rue de la Sourdière. Everyone howled threats or challenges. The guards muttered they would attack the Jacobins with cannon. During the tumult the members of the society left their hall. They were cheered and cat-called.

"Vive Robespierre!" some workers in short jackets suddenly yelled.

He had indeed appeared. Having left the meeting with the other Jacobins, he at that moment stood near the corner of Rue Saint Florentin. These shouts of his partisans precipitated a riot. Canes were raised, stones began to fly. Maximilien, standing motionless, faced the tumult. Meanwhile a man about fifty years old, of rough face and manners, his sleeves rolled up like a workman, had been standing on his doorstep watching the uproar. Suddenly he flung himself into the center of the fight. Seizing Robespierre by the arm, he dragged him away so quickly that everyone, Fayettistes and Sans-culottes, were dumbfounded. The door of his house slammed shut.

"Welcome to my house, citizen," said the man. "The

street is not safe. We will take care of you until tomorrow. This is Mme. Duplay, my wife, and these are my daughters and my son. In a minute you will see my nephew Simon, who wants to be a soldier. As for me, citizen, I'm Maurice Duplay, a cabinetmaker by trade, and at your service. . . ."

Before accepting so open-hearted an invitation, Maximilien had to overcome his characteristic reserve. But he remained. The following morning he thanked his host and wished to return home, to the Marais. But the entire family loudly protested against it. He shouldn't dream of going. All over Paris the rumor ran that he was about to be arrested. Without doubt the police were already waiting for him in Rue de Saintonge.

"Our hospitality is extremely modest," said Mme. Duplay. "But at least it is safe. In behalf of the people whom you love, we beg you to stay with us a few days."

Maximilien decided to remain. He felt that he was loved and admired by these honest folk, who were eager to render him every care. In that heart of his, which everyone believed was shut to human weakness, there always existed a kind of anxious and bashful tenderness. Those who did not know him well found great difficulty in explaining how such a sweetness of temper could ally itself with such dryness of disposition. And how this man, so firm, so intractable in all his dealings, could show an inner nature that was as docile as a lamb. . . . He remained. No longer would he take his key and his candle from his host at the Marais. His meager belongings, his books and his papers, were moved over to Duplay's house by the errand boy.

I learned all this from his sister Charlotte's lips. The letter, which she drew from her writing table to show me, also contained other news. Maximilien, having fulfilled his commission as deputy, and moreover, being worn out with fatigue, planned to take a little rest at Arras in his his house and among his family.

Robespierre at Arras!

Now, thought I, our worthy lawyers and the salons will raise a beautiful outcry. Still, it would amount to nothing if only the people themselves would display some sympathy toward my friend's early success. Alas, with considerable shame I confess that I feared Maximilien would receive the worst kind of reception from his fellow citizens. I had been so thoroughly persuaded that all Arras scorned their "patriotic agitator" that I was prepared for the worst. And, besides, had not Maximilien enjoined secrecy concerning his trip? Yet the city had somehow gotten wind of it, and now nothing else was talked about.

What was there to say? What was there to do? For a while I thought of diverting Maximilien from a project that I regarded as extremely dangerous. Fortunately I acted wisely and held my tongue. Ah! I still blush at my stupid fears. For never did a city fête its native son more lavishly. Never did the nose of envy and scandal receive a prettier snub. But I must describe the incidents of the day in detail.

We expected Maximilien on the 13th of October. A last post informed us that he was planning to stop a few hours at Bapaume. We went there to meet him. The coach arrived, but no Maximilien. Charlotte and Augustin began to be alarmed. The patriots of the district who gathered around us were not less disappointed. They were at a loss what to do with the civic wreath they had woven in honor of the Incorruptible. But a national guardsman coming from Paris that same morning informed us that Robespierre had been detained at the Jacobins the evening before, by a deputation from the Faubourg Saint Antoine. From this soldier we learned also that a mob had gathered at the doors of the Constituent Assembly on the evening it adjourned, to carry in triumph through the streets Robespierre and his friend Pétion.

Upon this news, we returned to the hotel, escorted by all the patriots of Bapaume, who carried their wreath and sang, "Ça Ira."

The next day he arrived.

With what pleasure we greeted each other! Upon seeing us, Maximilien, accompanied by Pétion, leaped to the road, and pressed us one by one to his breast. Emotion made us speechless. Augustin laughed and wept. Charlotte, more controlled, wiped the traveler's face. As to Pétion, he smiled and bowed to the cheers of the patriots of Bapaume.

A harangue by the municipality put an end for a short while to our transports. While the orator spoke, I watched my friend. I found him thin and pale, with lines of fatigue spreading like a veil over his face. His eyes, weaker than usual, seemed unable to bear daylight. He listened attentively to the speech addressed to him. He was simply dressed, but with extreme care, in a coat of olive green and a vest of silk. He wore dark breeches and low traveling boots.

After the palaver and the presentation of the wreath, we were scheduled to attend a banquet. When this was ended, we returned to our carriages. Ten or twelve of them escorted us, driving along toward Arras at a brisk trot, in a cloud of dust.

At a half league from the village, a veritable mob awaited Pétion and Robespierre. There were bouquets of flowers, songs and music. We proceeded at a snail's pace, in triumphal march, with two hundred horsemen escorting the carriage. Toward the end of our ride, at evening, the civic guards commenced to fire salvos, and with such effect that the patriots, now unharnessing their horses, imagined themselves already at the tiller of government. Maximilien opened the carriage door and descended, just as Mirabeau had done in Aix-en-Provence, the day he had, weeping, said to the people: "In this way one becomes a slave."

We then arrived on foot before the gate of Arras. Another mob was stationed along the ancient ramparts, at Saint Aubert's watering-place. The crowd packed Rue de l'Arsenal so tight that we had to shove our way into the narrow Rue du Pavage to reach the center of the city.

A reddish vapor rose above the steeples. From afar we had thought it was a fire. But those who escorted us had broken into laughter. This great, glowing light, this conflagration that rose to the sky, came from thousands of lamps in all the windows of Arras. Even the windows of the aristocrats were illuminated. Why did they celebrate? Maximilien thought they did so out of respect for popular will.

Old women, women dressed in white, awaited the conqueror at the threshold of his house. There were more harangues, and still more civic wreaths. For a last time, with full lungs, the mob roared: "Long live the Defender of the People!" And Robespierre entered his house.

He stayed there at home for six weeks. It was, in the endless tempest of his life, his only rest.

CHAPTER TWENTY

Brisk sea winds blew across our fields. Maximilien strode along the roads bordered with rusty brown trees. Breathing his native air again, he found his greatest pleasure in these walks through the plains, along the banks of the Scarpe. Evening would often find him lost on some old road, where water lying in ruts held leaden mirrors to reflect the paths of the clouds.

He often asked me to accompany him. It is said that he was afraid to be alone. During these forty days I was with him I learned to understand Robespierre better. Later I lived in close intimacy with him, in Paris, when I was afforded the opportunity of seeing him under other aspects, of approaching and analyzing a man born to astonish the world.

But it was in the rugged wastes of our countryside, swept by all the winds of the horizon, that the other Maximilien—the true one, perhaps—appeared to me. Unforgettable days they were! Side by side we walked in the wind, while he told me all the events of his two years of struggle. His success had not turned his head. He looked toward the future, with little thought of those obstacles he had surmounted, but with an eagerness to overcome others that were higher, more terrifying. He measured the danger.

"I have dedicated my life to truth!" he said.

Often he abandoned himself to the blackest forebodings. One day he confessed to me, in words that were both melancholy and serene, that he would almost accept death as a blessing, if it would save him from his inevitable misfortunes. Was he sincere? In this autumn of 1791 did he foresee his brief and eminent career? I believe he did.

Even at this time (when the struggle between parties still resembled the controversies of the scholastic fathers) he saw those days of fratricidal terror impending. He saw those bloody and murderous days approaching, which to so many others were sudden and hideous miracles. He could have avoided everything. But he loved his work—wholly, fiercely. In every way this task exceeding human strength cut short his life. For did he not himself know that, according to the cold and haughty prophecy of Saint Just, great men do not die in bed?

Was he ambitious? Certainly. Each day of his life found him more eager to triumph, to dominate. The incentive during his youth was that unyielding pride of the downtrodden which made his soul avid for power and grandeur.

The enemies of Maximilien Robespierre believe they discount his fame by portraying him in colors of ambition. After thirty years the survivors of those struggles still besmirch this inexorable ghost. How can one answer these puling dotards when neither history, worldly experience, nor their own errors can teach them that ambition is the propelling force behind all great political actions? Does ambition invariably deprive a statesman of all devotion to the public good? Those whose hearts are not set on power are weak leaders, the lazy, or swindlers. But neither great tyrants nor great revolutionists shrink from action before the tears of the conquered or the blood of factions. In times of crisis men are led only by those who can shut their eyes upon humanity.

That Robespierre followed the path of tyranny unflinchingly, I for my part have no doubt. Yes, he was a tyrant, if tyranny in action can also be respect for law. In the task of his terrible dictatorship he sacrificed everything, the simpler joys of life, his dearest friends, the immortality of his name. Alas, even I was estranged on the day I first saw that bloody cloud arise, which obscured his fame. It first appeared in October, 1793, with his attack upon the Girondins; it ended after the death of Danton. And how eternally fateful was his error! I do not reproach him for the blood. No. He did not kill. Search elsewhere for fratricides. But he could have withheld their arms. He let them kill. That is enough. O Robespierre, dear Maximilien, pure man! You should not have lent so complaisant an ear to the people's voice. Their lips whispered only counsels of pride. Unhappy man, they have deceived you, they have led you astray. In those triumphant days of Prairial when, acclaimed by the multitude, you walked beneath flowers, you were then only a headless phantom. If you were great, it was in the terrible desert of Thermidor, when, alone against the world, denied by your friends, betrayed, reviled, bleeding, they flung you into the cell at the Conciergerie, to lie there till they dragged you to the scaffold, amid the vituperation of a people to whom you had given everything.

The people! Maximilien sacrificed his life to them, his heart, even his fame, with a passion that drives men to great crimes. If only he had not always been the Incorruptible, solitary and without weakness! If only he had not remained loyal to that rigorous ideal which bases happiness on obedience to a sovereign will which emanates from the people itself! His dream was of a geometric perfection. When I objected to the ignorance, egotism and meanness of mankind, he looked at me sadly.

"What!" he exclaimed. "If we should substitute laws for oppression, would not mankind find happiness in the hate of evil and in the love of country?"

Such was his language. And all that pandered to the selfish pleasures of the mob outraged him as much as a selfish betrayal of public welfare. In his eyes it was contemptible to offer complete license to the people. Liberty appeared an austere idol to him. To Robespierre tolerance and anarchy were one and the same thing. "Harden Liberty's heart"—as his dearest disciple once remarked to him.

One stands amazed before the judgments Robespierre's contemporaries have passed upon him. One is astonished and terrified at the small number of people who are able to attribute other than simple domestic virtues to great men. One can be sure that his memory suffers less from his slanderers than it does from those apologists, who never grow weary of praising his scruples, his nicety, his frugality, his decency, his passion for work. Imprudent friends they are, who do not realize they praise a great leader only for those virtues which do not exceed the simple duties of a citizen. They judge him by the criterion of a common man. And thus, believing they defend him, O niggardly admirers, they expose to the mob's anathema those moral deformities which are the very conditions of greatness. Why do they not read their Bossuet? Why do they not contemplate those words of his on the "restless and audacious spirits who seem born to change the world?"

Is not a politician of vigilance and cunning necessarily a profound dissembler? The *Cur ego singularis ambularem* of the Ancients can apply only to those whom destiny has carried above their fellow men. In both public and private life, Maximilien wore a mask; a feigned impassiveness served his purpose, as well as a deliberate assumption of demagogy.

In reality, this sensitive-hearted man was actuated by the highest motives. He revered liberty, but he profoundly hated that moderation in government we now call "liberalism," which he considered only a lazy and hypocritical form of anarchy. Enslaved to the *"contrat social,"* he certainly believed, deep in his conscience, that it was one's duty to arrest the authority of law when national safety was endangered by it. He certainly believed that democracy was not possible in France for many years to come. Following his master Rousseau, he believed that in order to extend the activity of government, it was necessary to concentrate authority in the hands of one or two of its members.

The strangest nonsense in the world has been written on the political ideas of Robespierre. Political parties have in turn canonized and abhorred him. The Royalists themselves have asked each other if the Incorruptible did not work in defense of the Crown, and they have set a burlesque legend in motion, displaying Robespierre in the aspect of a rising protector, ambitious of marrying Madame Elizabeth, sister of the King. At the other extreme the Babouvists[1] have laid claim to him. M. Buonarotti, the descendant of Michel Angelo, who was often at the Duplays' and whom I have known personally, represents him as the forerunner of Socialism. What an error! To make it truth, it would be necessary to tax Robespierre with hypocrisy!

He was a man of peace and order; he believed that society must be built in the form of a pyramid. Not once did he admit the necessity of destroying the social hierarchy. Do you say he clung to the prejudices of his century? I reply that Maximilien was not a man to

[1] Babouvism, or the doctrine of Francois Babeuf, demanded the common ownership of property and a law requiring that everyone should work. *Tr.*

surrender them anything. And if you bring forward his pacific attitude on the eve of the insurrections, I will insist he accepted popular convulsions only as a means, not an end.

To him the usefulness of revolution was its destruction of the egotism, the cupidity and the blindness of the ruling classes. The demands of an angry people, even when they are excessive, retard the progress of oppression from century to century. Revolution alone has the terrible and sacred power of destroying slavery. But Robespierre knew that social upheavals are always without a future, and that immediately after the world slowly and surely swings back to its old injustices. His political ideal was to organize this work for the time, to rigorously compensate the inequalities of birth by the wisdom of law. This he expressly stated on many occasions. He always defended property. And equality, wrongly understood, was to him only an "extravagant imposture, a phantom held up before stupid men by the perverse," [2] and "used only by rogues to terrify imbeciles." [3]

I affirm that Maximilien placed the principle of authority above everything. During his trip to Artois, though he was considered one of the leaders of the Republican Opposition—the other being Pétion—he proved himself more Royalist than many of the aristocrats. He said:

"A nation can be free under a monarch. But I do

[2] Defender of the Constitution. No. 4.
[3] Speech on the Declaration of Rights.

not wish factions to rule under the name of a powerless king."

His adherence to peace in one way militated against him, during those tragic hours when his antagonists spoke for public peace in order to disturb it with impunity. It is said that he looked into the future when he affirmed:

"I do not believe that truth, justice or courage cause the downfall of nations, but intrigue, weakness, stupid credulity, corruption, the neglect of principles."

Thus honor and his political actions were never separated in his mind. If he wished to increase his glory, and if he marched resolutely toward this end, it was because he firmly believed he was predestined, because he built everything on virtue, and because he proved that a man was able to be both ambitious and unselfish at the same time.

I recall a profound and cynical phrase of Danton's: "It is said money frightens Robespierre." Indeed, he whose life I am writing believed that poverty and simplicity of manners should be the rule of all great lives. He believed it with intense fervor. Little by little, as his conscience affirmed itself, he began to consider virtue as an abstract principle and, in order to act, he placed himself outside accepted morality, outside humanity itself. Too self-assured, raising the conformity to one's principles above everything, he finally lost that salutary doubt, that uncertainty, which is the true mark of human minds.

Those who betrayed him later, those members of the

Mountain [4] who delivered him up to the counter-revolution, never felt this grandeur in him except confusedly. They realized only that it was beyond their range. Like these men, the whole course of the Revolution, moreover, required five years to swing toward his line of thought, which had never varied. Robespierre realized that the most terrible hate he had to endure, that of his dissatisfied followers, like Collot and Billaud—he knew this hate sprang from misapprehension. He had known it for a long time.

Many times did forebodings escape him. At the time of my story he confessed them to me, as we wandered along those old roads he was never to see again.

Though Robespierre strode on toward his defeat and his proscription, he did not move blindly, as certain historians have believed and written. Like Sylla he was able to descend alone and unarmed into the forum and pay for his abdication with his life. Two months before his death he had told those who loved him, "You will not see me for much longer." But he accepted to the end that appalling fate to which all great makers of history are sentenced.

[4] The Mountain was the party which comprised the extreme popular leaders and the Jacobins. Danton, Marat and Robespierre himself were members. *Tr.*

CHAPTER TWENTY-ONE

I HAVE transgressed the duty I outlined for myself. As a simple biographer, a modest eye-witness, I should have permitted the pen of thinkers and judges to lie unused on my desk. But how could I resist recalling those days and those conversations, which remain so pure in my mind? I must show Maximilien as he appeared to me then, complete—in his wisdom, in his conscience, in the integrity of his character. Let me be pardoned my digression. Hereafter I will not wander from my story.

Paris called Maximilien back to her. Each day the post brought him more pressing entreaties to return. He resisted. He delayed his departure. To everyone, including himself, he offered all manner of good excuses for remaining. With deep feeling he spoke of his native province. Certainly there were few enough memories which might endear him to it. He had lived there during the worst days of his childhood and his orphaned youth. There he had passed the joyless years of his early career as a lawyer, surrounded by hostile associates and judges who were shocked by the boldness of his pleas.

All those people who in the happy tumult of his return had swallowed their hate now became emboldened. An overture Robespierre had made toward a certain M. D. de F——— was returned by a polished affront. Shortly before the Revolution, my friend had rendered a few good services to this country squire. This affront and some malicious talk which happened to reach his ears brought him to a decision. He resolved to leave us.

During his visit I thought I noticed that he liked to pat my dog, "Broun." So I offered him to Maximilien. The evident pleasure he showed in accepting him proved to me that I had not been mistaken.

Finally, on the 27th of November, we accompanied Maximilien to the coach. In the midst of cheers and bravos he climbed aboard, after tenderly embracing us.

He was never to see the steeples of Arras again.

CHAPTER TWENTY-TWO

WAR was coming.

It was all anyone talked about. "Giddap! The Prussians!" cried the carter to his donkey. In the debating halls of the cities it was discussed at length. With arguments as limpid as daylight every orator proved to boobies and old women that foreign monarchs were eager to destroy the French for having imprisoned Louis when he tried to escape to his cousins. Cannons, bayonettes—to deliver mankind! At the Jacobins, Isnard, brandishing a sword, got himself cheered to the echo. Danton raised the trumpet of warning to his lips.

The war was coming.

It was all they talked about at the meetings of the new Assembly, from which, by the will of Robespierre, all the constituents, including himself, were excluded. A party was formed, which dominated the Assembly. They were the Girondins.

They wanted war. They asked for it with lyricism, with war chants intermingled with politics. The tribunes on which they mounted were illumined with the flashing of steel. Brissot, Fauchet, Condorcet, Guadet, went before the Jacobins crying, "To arms!" The Club applauded.

The uproar of preparations filled the nation. The Faubourg Saint Antoine forged pikes, made flaming tricolored banners, and carried all in great warlike array to the Bishop's Palace.

Out of sheer pleasure, drums were beaten. "Sacred Palladium! Swords! Scabbards! Crusades! Victories! Flags!" All voices joined in an heroic chant. Suddenly, in the shouts of warriors, another voice was heard dropping slow, icy words like a threnody. It was the voice of Maximilien. He had returned. Still giddy from the wind and shouting, his coat covered with the dust of travel, he ran to the Jacobins. Already the rumor of his return had spread. He appeared. Upon seeing him the members of the society rose to their feet. Again transports, ovations, greetings.

"I make a motion," cried Collot d'Herbois, "that this member of the Constituent Assembly, justly called the Incorruptible, preside over this society."

Thunderous applause. Robespierre was carried to the chair. After that, speeches were resumed. He listened to the orators. Finally he rose, and slowly mounted the tribune.

His first few sentences did not reveal the depth of his feelings. Those who applauded him were struck by his seriousness. For in truth Robespierre understood the danger of these outbursts.

The Jacobins of the provinces had not displayed so great an eagerness to fly to the frontiers. They feared the hazards of war, and murmured, with bourgeois horse sense, that someone is always vanquished in battle, and if an inimical fate decided against France, the Revolution would be done for.

To this Maximilien added his own caution. "Our real enemy," he suggested, "is perhaps not beyond our frontiers. There are emigrés, but there are also traitors. To intoxicate the people with trumpet calls makes them forget the lessons of misfortune. The smell of powder must not be considered incense. Prudence! A country in revolution must wage only a holy war. It is not decreed. It is invoked. At such a time it is the rising of the masses against their crowned oppressors. At such a time the souls of the ancients themselves rise from their graves to lead the defenders of Freedom. But first let the foreign powers give the signal of battle. . . . Are we to surrender to the sovereigns of Europe the rôle of peace lovers and place all right and justice on their side?"

Two days later he uttered these words: "No policy of aggression. Armed to the teeth, we must await provocation."

And here began the struggle between the Gironde and Maximilien. It was a fight without mercy, cruel and violent. At the start it was fought over principles. Brissot spoke for the Girondins. He replied with fury to a speech Robespierre had delivered on the 18th of December. Three days later, Robespierre, mounting the tribune before the Jacobins, delivered that immortal speech on the war which will in future ages be the breviary of all defenders of peace.

"It is within the bounds of possibility that the motive of those who shout for war, and who would direct it, is not to destroy our enemies and the friends of absolute monarchy. . . . But no matter. . . . First you are saddling yourselves with the conquest of Germany. Then you would parade our triumphant army before all neighboring peoples, and you tell yourselves that this is a sublime idea, as if the fate of empires was determined by rhetorical figures.

"It is unfortunate that truth and good sense belie these magnificent predictions. It is in the nature of things that the progress of reason is slow. The most extravagant idea that can enter a politician's head is the belief that all a people need do to spread their own laws and constitution is to enter another nation with a sword. No one loves missionaries with guns. And the first natural reaction is to drive them out like enemies.

"Before losing yourselves in politics and in the lands of European princes, observe your own domestic conditions, put your own house to rights before you carry freedom elsewhere."

A peroration addressed to the coming generation completed his speech, which was printed at the expense of the society and circulated throughout France. . . . The galleries had wept.

CHAPTER TWENTY-THREE

For some time I was without any news of Maximilien. Arras had fallen back into its torpor. I dragged out my dull existence. In church and court the bourgeoisie commented with mournful voices upon current events. My troubles grew. Judges, solicitors, all my associates, annoyed me as much as they could. My legal practice was poor; clients had never exactly crowded my office. Thanks to the malignancy of my associates, I now saw the hinges of my door grow rusty. Little by little my savings melted away.

Again my brother Tiburce wrote me from Paris. Encouraged by an auspicious start, he had thrown himself with calculated daring into those speculations the times favored. Among the tribe of merchants he discovered many openings. Like so many others who had taken no part in recent events, he now boldly pursued the conquest of his own fortune. The state of my finances seemed to disturb him. He asked me for details, which I failed to send him, whereupon he had the insolence to inquire of one of my associates at the bar, who made no mystery of my financial embarrassment. This happened in the last days of February.

BOOK TWO

CHAPTER ONE

In the mail coach I re-read the following letter, which I had received from Tiburce:

"Dear Brother:

"I do not send you this letter by mail because M. B.—— of Arras, who recently paid me a visit, has been kind enough to take charge of it. I would have been less impatient in getting in touch with you, if certain circumstances had not made haste necessary. This is the reason: my enterprises have recently taken an excellent turn. I shall be able to divide my profits with some assistant who can give me his honest coöperation. If what I hear is true concerning the state to which these times have reduced your finances, you should no longer sacrifice your future but give a greater care to your interests. I am in a position, dear brother, to aid you in this worthy plan. Retirement from an honorary position is a sacrifice the Revolution holds due. What helps, however, to temper the loss is the knowledge that a just fortune repays those who employ themselves in behalf of the people.

"In short, I ask you to join me in Paris. Make haste! If I can in any way expedite your arrival, please instruct me. I embrace you, my brother, with the greatest tenderness. I await word from you impatiently.

"My address is 11 Rue des Lombards, section of Arcis.

"TIBURCE."

The coach traveled swiftly. Before noon we were at Peronne; we set off immediately in order to reach Roye by nightfall. In the monotonous rattle of loose bolts and windowpanes, I grew drowsy. The hoofs of the coach horses danced before me. Now and then we would meet some courier galloping along the road, or we would pass a smoking bivouac. Horsemen bound for Saint Quentin, toward the frontier, rode by. On the farms a general listlessness and torpor announced approaching war. We drove along stretches of mournful fields across which fled the shadows of clouds. Finally, toward three o'clock on the 18th of March, we entered Paris by way of the Faubourg Saint Denis. Street loafers watched our coach pass. Women laughed from the windows.

Tiburce was waiting for me in the court of the coach office. I had not seen him since I was a small child and did not know what he looked like. He recognized me by a sign that I had taken care to advise him of and rushed toward me wtih outstretched arms. I then saw a man of about fifty, powdered and curled, with broad shoulders and the build of a farmer. He was heavy, his eyes bright, his flabby cheeks slightly pockmarked. In his features I saw something of our dead father, but coarsened and twisted into an expression of cynicism that pained me. I experienced a feeling of uneasiness I was not able to repress. But my brother, without appearing to notice my trouble, embraced me, complimenting me on my health and my corpulence. He then directed that my baggage be unloaded and a hack called, doing all this with the noise and heartiness of a peasant. Though people stared at us, he, unabashed, thrust his arm through mine, and led me toward the hack.

Tiburce thus brought me to Rue Trousse-vache, behind the Cemetery of the Innocents. At the Hotel des Consuls I was given a room. When the porter had brought up my trunk, my brother took leave, telling me that he would return early the next morning. At six o'clock I ordered supper, and while it was being prepared, I wrote a note which I sent by a porter to Robespierre, 366 Rue Saint Honoré, in care of Citizen Duplay, cabinet maker.

CHAPTER TWO

JUST as I was finishing dinner I received a reply, brought by a young worker of an agreeable military bearing, with earrings, trousers of striped cotton, a cockade hat, and a small mustache.

He entered without ceremony, greeting me with the simplicity customary in those days. I returned his salute.

"Monsieur," said he, "my name is Simon Duplay, and I come in behalf of the Incorruptible, who, for lack of time, was unable to come here himself, which he regrets."

Then, taking a breath, he continued:

"I am, with your permission, to take you to the Jacobins. That's all, Monsieur. The message is finished."

Saying this, Maximilien's envoy delivered a military salute. I seized my hat, and we departed. Night had come, a cool March night which drove people into theaters and cafés.

As we walked along, Simon Duplay confided to me his desire of enlisting in the army, to defend the Revolution. He would have liked to enter his name at once so that he could leave in the first levies. Like everyone at the time, he spoke lightly and gayly of war. It was a question of punishing the emigrés, as well as carrying Liberty to the lands of despotism. A soldier of a triumphant army, he would extend our institutions from the Rhine to the Danube, and even into the very states of Gustave of Sweden. But Maximilien threw water on his fire.

"He will prevent war, you see if he doesn't," said my companion as he walked along. "He says that the enemies of the Revolution are not so far from home as to make the business of suppression a matter for generals. He believes the war is an intrigue of the Court. No doubt he is right, for of all the patriots he is the most enlightened."

At this assurance, which my young military friend accompanied with a sigh, we arrived at Rue de la Sourdiere. Having skirted some gloomy buildings, we stopped before a triple arch. It gave access to a paved court. A mob of people were crowding toward the doorway of a church with a small belfry and steep gables. Through four windows light shone onto the ground. In the semi-darkness a flag floated above the entrance. It was the Club of Jacobins.

"Let us enter," said my guide.

I noticed that cards were required at the door. Simon Duplay drew two from his pocket and showed them to a powdered doorman. We passed inside.

There were more than a thousand citizens present. A row of pikes and busts of Mirabeau, Jean-Jacques, Sidney, Mably and Franklin adorned the walls. In the center of the hall a stone taken from the Bastille was exhibited. It was very warm inside, although without the cold was rather sharp.

We had choice seats below the president's platform, just in front of the tribune.

It was a little after eight o'clock. Already the members were murmuring at the delay. Looking everywhere for Maximilien, I was told that it was customary for him to work in the chapel library up to the very time the meeting was called to order. Suddenly the sound of a trumpet stilled the uproar. A door in the chancel opened and some of the better known members of the Club entered. Of them all, Robespierre was cheered the loudest.

The president immediately took the floor. He was the Savoyard Coppet, author of the *Memoires de Mme. de Warens*. He spoke at great length and received scant attention.

Suddenly there was an excited movement in the assembly. People rose and shouted. Then followed a profound silence. Collot d'Herbois and Legendre stood up on their benches. A man about fifty years old, quite small, his face sunburned, with bluish cheeks, had just entered. This man continued at an even pace from the door to the rail which separated the president's chair from the tribune. Arriving there, he solemnly saluted the president.

It was Dumouriez, minister of war.

He had driven in a small coach from the Tuileries without escort, to appear in his general's uniform before the Club, where his name was often received with hoots and yells. The crowd, which loved this kind of bravado, applauded him.

Dumouriez requested permission to speak. It was

granted. Scarcely had he begun when a loud-mouthed fellow interrupted and, holding out a dirty red bonnet, cried:

"Since you pretend to be a friend of the people, you certainly can't refuse to wear their hat!"

"Certainly not," replied the general, tossing aside his cap and putting on the red bonnet.

Again the hall broke into applause. Dumouriez continued:

"Brothers and friends, every moment of my life will be devoted to the people's will. . . . A heavy burden rests on my shoulders. Brothers, help me to carry it. Let your journals give me all the advice they can. Tell me the most bitter truths. But repress all slander and do not reject a citizen whom you know to be sincere and brave."

"Citizen," replied Coppet, "the Society feels itself honored in counting you among its members."

There were groans and bravos. The assemblage was divided. A coarse-looking man, who, I had learned, was the butcher Legendre, made a few discourteous remarks, and Collot sprang up protesting. Then I observed Maximilien. After calmly polishing the lenses of his spectacles, which he finally adjusted without haste, he mounted the tribune and spoke:

"I am not one of those who believe it entirely impossible for a minister to be a patriot. The bauble of ministerial power vanishes when it is confronted by the people. The presence of no minister fills me with apprehensions for this Society. But I swear that at the instant he obtains more power than a simple citizen, I shall demand his expulsion from this group."

Robespierre was silent for a moment. Then, regarding the general, with an icy smile he added:

"But that necessity will never arise."

He descended. Dumouriez at once flung himself into his arms. A roar of applause shook the vaulted ceiling of the chapel. Citizens wiped their eyes, and I confess for my part I felt deeply stirred.

Shall I continue a description of the rest of the meeting, when, after Dumouriez had departed, a discussion arose concerning the civic merits of phrygian caps? A letter from Pétion was read. Maximilien took the floor again. It was to condemn the intended insignia of militant equality and to praise the cockade. A vote was taken before the meeting adjourned at about half past two.

CHAPTER FOUR

THE next day at the hour we had agreed upon Tiburce came to the hotel. He took me out to lunch with him at the Sign of the Iron Man, a restaurant run by a native of Vanves, named Cordier.

A large number of substantial-looking citizens were present, but what species they belonged to I only too soon discovered. Before sitting down to table, they emptied many bottles of Auvergne, toasting one another noisily. Tiburce appeared very much at home. While lunch lasted I heard nothing but talk of provisions, markets and monopolies. All of them looked forward to the declaration of war. It seemed to be their one great hope, the Beulah Land of profits. Guns, horses, harness, wagons, provender, boots, shirts, stockings, provisions, coffins, would all be needed then. They flattered themselves that they could supply everything. While waiting, they ate and sopped up liquor.

The sight of them produced a strange feeling in me of disgust, shame and curiosity. I watched Tiburce. He seemed a swaggerer, rather than a scamp. The vicissitudes of his adventurous career, while coarsening his still vigorous and handsome features, had not entirely corrupted him. He smiled whenever he looked at me; I realized that to overcome my evident uneasiness he was forcing the conversation.

Finally lunch ended. Carriages were ordered and the band dispersed, each man to his little den in the alleys of Les Halles or the Temple.

Tiburce and I took a cab. But all during our drive I did not open my mouth. I remembered the words of Maximilien, and his brief advice. In spite of his brazenness, Tiburce did not know how to break the silence. Mutely we drove through Great and Little Montrouge, past the Observatoire, through Faubourg Saint Michel. By way of Rue d'Enfer and Rue de la Harpe we reached Pont du Change.

Towards four o'clock we arrived at the Hotel des Consuls. Tiburce tried to pay the cabby, but I stopped him. Finally, without having exchanged a single word, we entered my room. Then a conversation ensued which left each of us more distant than when I had believed him in the galleys or dead. One can understand my repugnance in writing about this painful subject. But for the sake of clearing up subsequent events, I must.

I will limit myself to saying that Tiburce represented that type of petty swindler every epoch of unrest produces. What he proposed I should do for him enraged me. Was I so naïve, he asked, as to refuse to profit through my connections?

As for Tiburce, he amassed a considerable enough fortune to enjoy in his declining years the esteem of those persons who are most intolerant of a poor man's deviation from strictest honor. He died decorated by the Empire. . . . I will be brief. As soon as I learned what type of man I was dealing with, and for what services he hoped to reward me, I ordered him, without further ado, to leave.

I heard his footsteps reëcho on the stairs. I saw him cross the main highway and make toward Rue Quincampoix. I at once dispatched another note to Duplay's house. I wished to see Maximilien without delay, to prove to so scrupulous a friend that I was not below his respect. Within an hour Maximilien replied with a friendly note, and though he did not arrange an interview, the messenger at the same time handed me an invitation from Mme. Duplay, who simply and pleasantly expressed the wish of counting me henceforth among the regular guests at her home. She received every Thursday, in other words, that same evening.

I put on my best clothes. After supper I took my way toward the worthy lady's home.

CHAPTER FIVE

HUMBLE refuge, a retreat for wise men. I had seen the Incorruptible's room. I had seen the tiny study in which the little lawyer, the laughing stock of the Court, measured one by one those words which were to make a king's head fall. I saw that lamp whose pale and somber light watched late in the slumbering faubourg. I saw the lead inkwell, the windowpanes, the spruce shelves, the chair of coarse straw, the bed covered with cheap blankets.

During our walks along the banks of the Scarpe, when Maximilien had described his attic room a doubt had disturbed me that I must confess here. I was suspicious of my friend's sincerity. He displayed his privations, thought I, too complaisantly; he laid his colors on a bit too thick. In a word, he took too easy an advantage of *Res sacra miser*. However, I was mistaken. Maximilien had described his indigence too modestly. His lodgings were well below his description of them. In fact, a lawyer's clerk or a porter would scarcely have been content in his room.

His only window overlooked a tiny court where from morning to evening resounded the noise of hammers, saws and planes. The workers' tool shed was just under the floor, while the overhang of the roof shut out light from the window. Two pots of flowers concealed a zinc pipe, which, fastened with iron bands, carried the rain water from the eaves to the gutter. Laundry was drying on a clothes line. Above the walls and the trees one could see the little clock of the Jacobins and the cupola of the Church of the Assumption. Birds crossed the open space, and now and then the sound of bells would drown out the noise of the workshop. . . .

So, on this Thursday evening, I paid my first visit to the Duplays. When I neared the house, I found young Simon waiting for me. The vaulted alleyway we entered led to a dark courtyard. At the far end, toward which we proceeded, was a window whose bluish curtain veiled a clear, soft light. This was the salon of Mme. Duplay. At the sound of our steps the door was opened.

Maximilien stood leaning against the mantelpiece. A fire of wood shavings crackled on the hearth, where "Broun," whom I had given Maximilien, lay curled up asleep. Maximilien was motionless. A mirror behind him reflected his shoulders, the high collar of his coat, and his powdered pigtail. He was speaking, but my entrance interrupted him, and, taking off his glasses, he recognized me. Then, crossing the room and warmly grasping my hand, he introduced me to everyone present.

The salon of the cabinetmaker was well filled. Mme. Duplay stood at the end of the room near the harpsichord between her two daughters, Elizabeth who was called Babet and Eléonore who was called Cornélie. Her son, whom Maximilien referred to as "our little Patriot," was standing near the window. On chairs of mahogany upholstered in red velvet a quiet group of people were ranged in a semicircle. There, for the first time, I saw Camille Desmoulins with his gracious and gentle Lucille. Beside her sat a woman who made eyes at Maximilien. I was told she was the old Marquise de Chalabre, obsessed with politics, mannish, much taken with Robespierre, and an endless source of merriment to the Aristocrats.

Next to her sat Santerre's brother-in-law, Panis, who played an important rôle in the life of Maximilien. Then two artists, David and his pupil Gérard, he who had painted the full-length portrait of Robespierre which dominated the room. Anthoine, a cold, delicate man, another lodger of Mme. Duplay's, stood next. Finally, standing near the entrance was a group of five men gathered around old Duplay, who, in spite of his heavy beard, showed a jovial face and rosy cheeks. These men were Vaugeois, Mme. Duplay's brother; the Jacobin, Sergent; the linen dealer, Taschereau de Fargues; and two jolly men in greatcoats and velvet collars named Nicolas and Didier, both printers.

The conversation I had interrupted by my entrance was resumed. The session of the Jacobins on the evening before was being discussed. Maximilien, always suspicious of military men, did not conceal the fact that he felt certain scruples of conscience in giving Dumouriez his support. He considered him to be not less suspect than

Lafayette. David undertook a defense of the general, while Camille Desmoulins regarded him as an adventurer useful to the Revolution.

The discussion became warmer. War was finally mentioned which here, as in all other places, occupied men's minds. Robespierre cut this conversation short. Another subject interested him more, a dispute he knew was imminent between himself and the Girondins on belief in God. A speech he was preparing contained the word "Providence," which he had repeated often and intentionally. He realized that against the Jacobins the extremely atheistic party of the Gironde would raise violent and bitter protest.

"To rise toward virtue," said he, "feeble humanity must use the wings of faith. Those illustrious men who are our guiding spirits believed in God, and should we dare deny the idea of an Eternal Being?"

He reflected a moment, and then continued:

"Oh! I can cope with them!" he cried. "I know that Guadet and without doubt Brissot will address the assembly on this."

"They will cry your speech down as a *capucinade,*" said Panis.

"No," said Robespierre. "That is an expression all patriots, even Girondins, would reject with disgust."

And then in his most cutting tone, he added:

"Atheism is the boast of Aristocrats."

The door opened. A little man with a red face, high cheekbones and a sharp nose, with something over-sweet and hypocritical about him, stood in the doorway. Having shaken the rain from his hat, he bowed.

"Come in, Legendre. Have a chair," Duplay shouted to him.

He was the butcher, the defender of Danton. Having again bowed to each of us, he sat down beside Mme. Duplay without further ceremony. As for me, I remained in a corner behind my friend, speaking little and hearing a great deal. Elizabeth Duplay, who was a musician, placed herself at the harpsichord. She played and sang the beautiful and exalted hymn of Gossec.

"Sing again, friend," said Maximilien, when she had ended.

She did not require pleading. Until the end of the evening, at eleven, her song ravished us.

As people were leaving, Maximilien led me to one side:

"What do you think you'll do?" he asked abruptly.

"I don't know."

"Practice law?"

"No."

"You're right. Anxiety for the public good has diverted all our young lawyers from court. Only the second rate and the bearded egotists remain. Besides, business flags there. All things considered, I advise you to find a position elsewhere."

"But where?"

"At the Society, if you wish."

"I am not a Jacobin."

Maximilien bit his lips. I added:

"It would be better if I were, would it not?"

Without replying, he said to me briefly:

"Come."

And he led me to his room. There he studied me a moment fixedly, shaking his head. Suddenly dropping his melancholy expression, he broke into laughter.

"Feuillant!" said he. "So you're a moderate, and perhaps even worse than one. Oh, well. I'm not the ogre people say I am, and you will see that I'm not. You will be neither a Jacobin, nor a Jacobin's clerk. After all, you are true to your profession. The odor of court clings to you. Become a judge."

"You are mistaken, Maximilien; I am neither *feuillant* nor Fayettiste. I am a patriot. I love the Revolution with all my soul and, even in jest, you are wrong to hold my patriotism in suspicion. But the Jacobins of Arras have cooled my zeal for the Society."

"What do you mean?"

"Nothing you do not already know. Haven't I written to you about it? Men such as Desmaux, Roux-Roux, and Fichère the watchmaker, through their excesses do great hurt to the people's cause. . . ."

He cut me short and said:

"I despise demagogues."

"I know it."

"And they hate me."

"Without doubt they do. But their hatred does not make impossible the intention of the wisest among them of abandoning you, while pretending to support you. And are you certain those Jacobins at Arras are the only ones who have recourse to this imposture? Is it not even true of those at Paris? I speak to you frankly, you see, as loyalty demands that I do. Ah, Maximilien, grant an old friend license to warn you that advice is worth much more than flattery."

"Thanks. You are right," said he. And he added, "Patience!"

His face had suddenly darkened into an expression of almost morbid distrust. He stared down into the shadows of the courtyard, then moving to the center of the room, he stood motionless in a strange absorption. He seemed to have forgotten my presence. Suddenly he turned toward me.

"Yes, you are right, and I do not doubt your patriotism. Count on your friend. It is getting late and I have work to do. My heart is for those I love but my strength belongs to the Revolution."

Saying these words and relapsing into his thoughtful mood, he gave me his hand, which I seized. He shook his head again and seated himself wearily. We were alone in his room, where a strong odor of rosin prevailed. We remained silent. After a moment we heard Mme. Duplay calling up from the courtyard:

"Here are your lamps, Maximilien. Everything is ready."

Maximilien rose.

"Adieu," he said.

I descended to the courtyard. Mme. Duplay, a lamp in hand, awaited her lodger at the foot of the stairs.

"I must bid you good night, Madame," said I.

"We will see you next Thursday, Monsieur?"

Then came the voice of Maximilien.

"Call him Monsieur the Judge, mother. He will be one in a few hours."

CHAPTER SIX

WAR was coming. Everyone demanded it. Alone against all, obstinate and impassible, Robespierre still stood out against the decree of war. Would he prevail against the enthusiasm of one side and the intrigues of the other? The Girondins began to show their teeth. They carried their attack into the Jacobin Club itself. One evening a little man of fair complexion, breezy and witty, appeared on the tribune of Rue Saint Honoré. He was Louvet, the author of *Faublas*. His tongue lashed Robespierre with a wit and bitterness that made him furious. The attack had stemmed from Brissot. Camille Desmoulins took upon himself the business of evening things up, and public criers went shouting from faubourg to faubourg:

"Read Brissot Unmasked, by Camille Desmoulins, attorney-general of the lamp post.[1] For four sous, Parisians!"

Brissot did not accept defeat. Instead of replying to Camille, he set himself on Robespierre, who he had good reason to believe inspired the pamphlet. His journal, *le Patriote Français*, published:

"There are three opinions the public shares on M. de

[1] The lamp post was the symbol of lynch law. *"A la Lanterne!"* was a mob cry of denunciation. *Tr.*

Robespierre. One group believes him crazy; a second attributes his conduct to wounded vanity; while a third believes his name is on the King's payroll. For ourselves, we never believe in corruption till it be well proved."

At the Jacobins, Maximilien replied to the attack and did so with a quietness that made some people turn cold.

"I forgive your slanders," said he, referring to his enemies. "But remember that Patriots judge you and that no consideration will keep the friends of their country from fulfilling their duty."

A while before he had spoken of "making the sword of law move horizontally to smite off the heads of certain leading conspirators!"

But the Girondins did not consider themselves beaten. Guadet took the tribune at the Assembly and suggested ostracism of Robespierre and his followers. The old women knitting in the gallery were outraged.

"Scoundrels! Rascals!" they screamed.

Hate was entering people's hearts. And war was drawing near.

It was at this time Robespierre had an interview with Marat. The friend of the people had returned from his escapade in Normandy, harassed and enflamed. A cabriolet had picked him up in the dead of night at Beauvais and had dropped him off in the very midst of the square in which public executions took place.

What happened at this meeting with Marat, Robespierre never divulged. I have heard it said that Marat flew into a passion.

"You are talking in the air," Maximilien might have said. And the pamphleteer might have rejoined, "I am not one of those icy souls who can see the sufferings of others without pity." At any rate, they returned from the interview so discontented with each other that at the Jacobins Robespierre accused Marat of extravagance and fanaticism, while Marat's journal, the *Ami du Peuple,* printed: "An interview which I just had with Robespierre confirms me in my opinion that he unites the intelligence of a wise senator with the integrity of an honest man. But he at the same time lacks the vision and daring of a real statesman."

Discord was everywhere. The first rumbling of cannon was mixed with mutterings of another storm. Men came to blows and to murders. Grangenouve was thrashed in the gardens of the Tuileries. Colonel Jancourt seized Chabot by the throat. Poniards were being whetted for d'Esprémesnil and Le Pelletier.

Danton ridiculed Maximilien's nightly gatherings, which he called a "Walpurgisnacht of Spanish-American Jesuits"; Eléonore Duplay he dubbed "Cornélie Copeau." The Queen said to Dumouriez, "Your existence depends upon your conduct." Marat crawled back into his secret cellars. The journal *Le Père Duchesne* accused the generals of playing with their toes. Louis XVI, an amateur locksmith, devised hidden safes to conceal proofs of his intrigues.

On the morning of April 23, Théroigne de Méricourt, perorating from the balcony of the Feuillants, cried out

CONTEMPORARY CARTOON OF ROBESPIERRE.

that she retracted all her support of Robespierre. The Girondins, who surrounded her, cheered. That same evening she proceeded to the Jacobins. Collot d'Herbois jested about her speech, and the whole Club rocked with laughter. Théroigne jumped onto the rail and screamed a reply. They bundled her out into the street.

The next day I lunched at Duplay's house. Maximilien, peeling some oranges, of which he was very fond, expressed pity for Théroigne.

"Oh, she isn't worth troubling about," Duplay interrupted.

Romme, who was lunching with us, said:

"Hate enters people's hearts."

"Revolutions," said another voice, "begin with speeches and end with swords."

"Is it indeed you, Camille, saying that?"

"No. It is Marat."

The following morning the *Chronique de Paris* published this piece of news:

"Yesterday, at half past three in the afternoon, the machine to cut off the heads of condemned criminals was put in operation for the first time." [1]

[1] The guillotine was not invented by the good doctor whose name it has immortalized. It had been in use for more than a century in Italy and in the Midi. It was, however, largely through Dr. Guillotine's endeavors adopted by the National Assembly on the grounds of humanity. Until that time executions had been performed by swordsmen. The introduction of the guillotine transformed executions from a fine art to an industry. *Tr.*

CHAPTER SEVEN

I WAS a justice of the peace, with two judiciary assessors, and two olive branches in silver. I rendered ineffectual justice in the old house of the Blancs-Manteaux, Rue de Paradis. I was not compelled to wait for my appointment, for since the emigration the judiciary, like the army and navy, had been scattered. The sentences I passed were made ridiculous because there were only process servers in revolutionary jackets to execute them. Moreover, both plaintiff and defendant were thoroughly convinced of the nullity of the proceedings. As for me, when I had adjourned court, I strolled aimlessly and alone about the streets.

So it was that, on the 20th of June, I saw the crowds returning from the Tuileries where by way of celebrating the third anniversary of the Tennis Court Oath they had just enjoyed a splendid riot.

Having stuck the *bonnet rouge* on the King's head and drunk wine with him, the mob was now returning as gay as larks. Everything had proceeded very well—a thousand cheers, a speech, and no blood. It was an uprising entirely after the hearts of the Girondins, who, in fact, had arranged it. Everyone laughed except Louis, who as soon as he reëntered his own apartments had trampled the cockade and the red hat under his feet.

It was a little after seven. In Rue Saint Antoine they formed a parade which included everyone—musicians, disabled soldiers, children, charcoal-sellers, pike-men, beggars, charlatans, and even a criminal, who seemed gloomy and depressed by the whole business.

The mob was jubilant under its pikes, its long handled knives, its blunderbusses, its skewers, its iron clubs, its placards. Santerre circled about in the midst of the throng, at his side the citizen, Marquis de Saint Hurughe, heavily disguised as a greengrocer, and a tiny officer named Mouchet, so short that his cape trailed along the ground. Santerre, whose voice was famous, led the mob in the song "Ça ira."

Farther off, among a number of workmen who were dancing about and brandishing bottles, I recognized the butcher, Legendre. He seemed swollen with pride, having, in the name of the people, read the petition before the King, whom he had addressed as "Monsieur," and called "false-hearted." I saw also the hearts of calves, impaled on the points of sabers, with these words printed below them, "The Heart of an Aristocrat." A few groups were dragging cannon behind them. A dry summer dust, mixed with dung and smoke, enveloped the crowd, which winding past the ruins of the Bastille, trailed off in the direction of Quinze-Vingts, the asylum for the blind.

Maximilien, whom I saw that same evening, had not gone to the Tuileries. On the contrary, with Pétion,

Manuel and Sillery, he had attended a meeting to persuade Santerre against the uprising. Maximilien declared himself opposed to armed mobs. The anger of the militant brewer had not made Robespierre change his mind, and he had withdrawn from the meeting.

At this time he had something more important on his mind. For a month he had believed that in view of the obstinacy with which Louis intrenched himself behind his suspensive vetoes, the title of the Jacobin journal, "The Defender of the Constitution," was as dangerous as it was compromising. The Constitution! The King kept it in his pocket for good, with that page granting him his veto well marked. Still, that was not Robespierre's chief worry. He was watching Lafayette. For that general no longer concealed his overwhelming desire to break up the Jacobins.

The Jacobins! Robespierre believed with all his soul that to overthrow the Jacobins would be to crush the Revolution. Did not the vigilant and dreaded eyes of the monastery windows watch over the deeds of public men? Dared Lafayette close the Jacobins, whose president marched side by side with the president of the Assembly and who in official ceremonies was a step above the government's ministers? Close the Jacobins, the political school of the nation, which communicated pure patriotic dogma to its thousand branches! Compared to the moral authority of the Club, the power of the Assembly was as nothing. For the Club was the great director of the Revolution.

Robespierre presumed that in the future the power of the Jacobins would become greater still, that a day would arrive when no one, either in Paris or in the departments, would dare disobey the dictates of that society over which he ruled. And it was this organization Lafayette wished to destroy. Indeed, Lafayette had so little concealed his hate that, to speak against the Jacobins to the Assembly, he had deserted his post in the very midst of war.

The general, in fact, wished to do worse. He planned to put the Jacobins to flight at the point of the sword. A meeting had been arranged on the night of the 30th of June in the Champs Elysées. But the Queen, who bore a childish malice toward Lafayette since the October insurrection, and particularly since the failure of the royal flight to Prussia, would rather have perished than owe her safety to him.

The following day, at the Café of the Golden Sun near the Bastille, there was a reunion of desperate and sullen men, almost all unknown, who over a bottle of wine decided to capture the Tuileries.

CHAPTER EIGHT

THE insurrection of the 10th of August was brewing. As early as the 20th of July the anger of Paris had burst forth like an oath.

Strife rose before all, its face unmasked.

The 4th of August was the decisive day. Panis, who was Maximilien's man in the cabals, left Duplay's house about noon, to proceed to a secret meeting-place—a cabin in the midst of gardens. But no plan was matured there. For a second conference took place that evening at Anthoine's, that is to say, in Duplay's house.

That evening Maximilien was present in Duplay's salon with some friends, including myself. Signs of a storm hung over Paris. Low clouds streaked with lightning gathered ominously in the west. As the heat was stifling, all the windows were open. In Anthoine's room members of the directorate of the insurrection argued. Voices excited by wine rose and fell. Santerre, and Carra, above all, led the cries of the most violent faction. Toward midnight, Mme. Duplay could restrain herself no longer, and disregarding our protests, she knocked at Anthoine's door.

"Do you want Robespierre to get his throat cut?"

Anthoine replied brutally:

"If someone is to be butchered, it will be us. As for Robespierre, he has only to run away and hide."

Maximilien heard it, and shrugged his shoulders. A little while later, the noise ceased. We separated.

I scarcely reached my room in time. Since the famous night of the 14th of July, 1788, a storm like it had not been seen. The sky, split open by ceaseless flashes of lightning, trembled in an immense and luminous palpitation. Although the air was motionless, clouds rising from the horizon blackened the sky above us. Then suddenly the storm broke. Furious winds, unleashed in long squalls, mowed down everything before them, pent-houses and chimneys. Thunder rolled like the rumble of cannon in battle. In an instant the deserted streets were flooded with hail-lashed streams of rain. The next morning iron gratings were found in the street, ripped out with the blocks of stone that had anchored them. All the crosses in the squares from Saint Germain to Charenton were flung down. Milk men and gardeners perished along the roads. A sentinel at the gate of the Royal Court was found killed by lightning under the ashes of his sentry box.

Now, while the elements were unchained, while the water and fire of heaven disputed the ownership of space, the sound of a distant chorus reached my ears. I leaned from my window. The howling of the wind did not drown out the song. It drew nearer. It was coming from the Palais Royal. A hundred or so men were marching toward me in the street below. Splashing knee deep in the over-running gutters, bearing aloft their ships' lanterns, they marched on singing with full throats.

Their joy challenged the furies of the storm. Doors opened. People rushed out into the tempest to applaud these strange singers. For they were the men from the south, the Federated Marseillais, chanting their own song of Revolution.

CHAPTER NINE

I AM obliged to write that Robespierre played no part in the uprising of the 10th of August. His friends were astonished by his strange indifference to the feverish preparations. I speak of his Parisian friends. As for me, I was not surprised by his detached, abstracted air on the eve of civil war. Once again my observation of him at Arras was confirmed, when in the great days of the summer of 1788 I had seen him flee from popular celebrations and lock himself in his room to draw up his address to the public. He was not a man of the mob. He was not seen on the 13th of July in Camille Desmoulins' uprising, nor on October 5th which was Maillard's, nor on the 20th of June which was Pétion's, nor on the 10th of August which was Danton's, nor later on the 31st of May which was Marat's, nor on the 4th of September, '93, when Chaumette led the insurrection. He descended to the streets only once. That was on the 9th Thermidor, when he descended to die.

Was he a coward, as his enemies pretend? A contemptible slander! The survivors of those days can attest with me that Maximilien was very brave in the face of death. But he did not sympathize with the transports of crowds.

Contrary to Danton, who rode the mob as Neptune rides the storm, Robespierre always displayed a puritanical and bourgeois aversion toward riots and barricades.

However, he measured the popular forces to a nicety and well knew Revolution does not survive except through the incessant mingling of workers and dictatorial groups. I have always heard him maintain that the laws destined to assure happiness to the people should be voted under their eyes. In his speeches his sacrifice to sentiment was made less for his colleagues than for the galleries. In this, again, he differed from Danton, who spoke briefly before the Assembly but let his oratory loose in the city squares. Danton believed only in the street and made use of the assemblies. Robespierre based all on assemblies, but intimidated them with the street.

How can one explain this abhorrence of mob action in a man who was the spirit of Revolution incarnate? There is only one reason. Robespierre lived alone, worse than alone—for he hemmed himself in between walls of praise. Paris became used to accepting him as its chief, almost as its proprietor. But of Paris he knew hardly more than one street, the street in which all his life in Paris took place, the Club, the Assembly, his room. Like most men of abstract principles, he knew little of simple mortals and the inevitable pragmatism of their ideals. What Robespierre understood by the "people" was at bottom an abstraction. It is true he happened to live among the humble. But they were those of his own convictions. He saw them at the Jacobins or at Duplay's. As to the real mass of common people with their easy manners, their heartiness, their fickleness, their appetites, ignorance, mercy—if he had really known them he would have found them exasperating or even repellent.

Thus while the workers were afire with their preparations for another July 14th, Robespierre remained a man of speeches and the written word. It is said that he did not believe in the imminence of an uprising. That is possible, but it is not certain. At any rate it would be untrue to count him among the forces of the glorious insurrection. In the days which preceded it, he refrained from speaking often; only thrice did he mount the tribune of the Jacobins. His great speech of July 29th expressed his attitude. It is the attitude of a lawmaker, not of an insurrectionist. A single sentence might lead one to believe that Robespierre accepted the hypothesis of insurrection as a last recourse. Yet he made it the price of the one thing most desirable in his eyes: the fall of the King.

"The state must be saved, in any manner possible," he said. "That alone is unconstitutional which tends toward the state's destruction."

This apostrophe expressed in so parliamentary a language has misled certain enthusiasts, to whom Robespierre himself has given the lie. He was often heard to repeat:

"In that memorable uprising, the nation had many defenders more useful than I."

This declaration he flung later into Pétion's face, word for word, except that he replaced "I" with an "us." Only

Pétion and some close members of the salon Duplay were able to understand its full significance. . . .

There is no reason why I should here conceal the fact that Pétion called on Robespierre on the eve of that insurrection in which the former acted so oblique a part. On the evening of the 7th, Pétion unexpectedly appeared, a little before ten o'clock. As one who had been informed of it, he had chosen the night of an important meeting of the Jacobins. At this late hour what reason had Mayor Pétion to visit a citizen, who was influential, true, but without office, if it were not to prod him into advising members of the Jacobin insurrectional directorate to restrict themselves to certain legal and therefore deliberative precautions? Did Robespierre let himself be persuaded? History answers the question.

To complete my story of these days, I must mention the visit of handsome Barbaroux and Rebecqui. Panis brought them to the Duplays', where Robespierre received them in the salon. The day before, certain Jacobins, speaking covertly, had preached in favor of Robespierre and against Brissot to the two Marseillais. What effect had this had on them? The fact is that Rebecqui cut short Maximilien's words to say dryly:

"We're Republicans. We no more want a dictator than we want a king."

And both left, slamming the door behind them. Panis ran after them, shouting that they had misunderstood the matter. Robespierre departed for the meeting of the Jacobins, looking worried.

In certain books a ragged abbé has been mentioned as involved in this affair of the Marseillais. He is entirely a figure of romance. Except for Gregoire and Vaugeois, ecclesiastics were hardly ever seen in the house on Rue Saint Honoré. As for the rags, Mme. Duplay would never have suffered them in her house. She loved decency and good manners too much for that.

CHAPTER TEN

MADAME DUPLAY lived only for her lodger. It is probable that she admired him less as a statesman than she did as an irreproachable guest. For aside from his fame, Maximilien was endowed with those virtues of civility, exactitude, and sobriety, which every bourgeois French mother seeks in a son-in-law. The good woman believed, and frankly admitted, that Maximilien would have been a paragon of husbands.

This opinion was also shared, to perhaps even a greater degree, by the cabinetmaker himself, though his hopes had something more of pride in them. The marriage of his daughter Eléonore to the Incorruptible would have carried this pure Jacobin to the pinnacle of happiness. Less sanguine than Madame Duplay, he feared to abandon himself to his fond ambitions, though Maximilien, without involving himself one way or the other, did nothing which might discourage them.

In truth, Duplay could hope without appearing ridiculous. For inasmuch as he owned three houses, one on the Rue des Mathurins, another on the Rue de l'Arcade, and a third on Rue du Luxembourg, his daughter would not have made a bad match. Furthermore, his daughters placed, as it is said, "certain hopes in their uncles." Had he been less smitten by politics and less desirous of allying himself to the powerful men of the time, Duplay would not have had any trouble in marrying off his daughters well. Elizabeth in marrying Lebas was to be the first to experience the pleasure of hymen. Her elder sister waited without bitterness.

Eléonore Duplay, or Cornélie as her family called her, was twenty-one years old. She is still living. She passes through my memory like a sweet and mournful shadow.

Unhappy Eléonore, betrothed and bereaved, an old woman with the past of an unhappy child, I wonder about you, about those thirty years you have borne your dear secret amid hate and maledictions. I think of you, pale lover, faithful and lonely friend; I think of our meetings at the moldering graveyard of Errancis, and the remembrance of your face revives the sorrows of my old heart. . . .

Her features were regular and peaceful, full of the unassuming grace of a young bourgeoise. Though she loved and admired Maximilien, doubtless more respect than passion entered into her feeling for him. Nothing in the Incorruptible could inspire frivolity. Though he was no Lothario, there was something about his figure, his elegance, and his good breeding, which was extremely attractive. Though certain envious people have denied it, women were fond of him and many a one dreamed of sharing his perilous glory. When he spoke before the

Club or the Assembly, women filled the galleries and greeted his oratory with enthusiastic applause.

"And there are some," Condorcet wrote maliciously, "who ask why there are always so many women hanging round Robespierre: at his house, in the galleries of the Jacobins and of the Convention. It is because this revolution of ours is a religion, and Robespierre is leading a sect therein. He is a priest at the head of his worshippers; his power rests on distaffs."

This kind of success enraged Maximilien's rivals, who called his admirers "greasy skirts." But Danton refused to believe Robespierre had any success with women. Jeering at his engagement to "Cornélie Copeau," he accused him of sleeping with old women.

But whether young or old, whatever age they were, Maximilien's attention was directed elsewhere. I hardly dare say what I really believe about him, in an age like ours where chastity passes as a subject for stupid jokes. Nevertheless it is true that Maximilien was chaste to the point of prudery. Did he not have a falling out with Camille Desmoulins over a trifling matter concerning some obscene books? If all my opinions on the matter were asked, I should be rash enough to hazard the statement that Robespierre had never known love beyond a mild and sentimental feeling of gallantry.

What sentiment did he experience for Eléonore? People have never tired of asking me this question. Shall I try to answer? I shall not, for I know nothing about it. Robespierre refrained from confidences as being the lowest kind of familiarity. He observed an unbelievable modesty, and the audacity of asking him questions concerning his affections never occurred to anyone.

Toward Eléonore he displayed a friendship which, though it was constant and tender, was at the same time a little distant. His attitude was that of an older brother. But as he was thirteen years older than she, this can be explained by the difference in their ages. Moreover, those who were intimate with Robespierre attribute his coldness to other reasons. He was overworked. His duties and his struggles absorbed him entirely; he lived for his country, and those few moments when duty permitted him to dream were filled with the hopes and doubts of his high ambition.

Yet it is certainly true that he meant to marry Mlle. Duplay. He considered it a point of honor not only to fulfill all his promises but to satisfy desires he had not discouraged. Never in my presence did he ever make the slightest allusions to the betrothal, which by the Duplays was considered a thing concluded but deferred. Until when? The question contained its own reply. Robespierre's marriage to his host's daughter would in all certainty have crowned his final triumph. But until this triumph came, nothing would deter him, neither preliminary bonds, nor financial embarrassment. Nevertheless, the couple might have profited by the political retreat Maximilien made during the session of the Legislative Assembly. But they waited until the political struggles had ended. In the blaze of his triumph two years later, Maximilien again deferred his marriage, as if he still awaited a higher, a more complete, a more indestructible victory. But what victory? Let us abandon this enigma to the reflection of those who, believing they love and defend Robespierre, fear for his memory the majestic horror of the dictatorship.

CHAPTER ELEVEN

We are now in the days of the September massacres. On Sunday evening of the second of September, to the clamor of the tocsin the horrible business began. Aroused by the Prussian invasion and the capitulation of Verdun, a mob led by the Sections broke into the Abbey and *La Force* and slaughtered all the political prisoners they could find there. For four days, with unexampled brutality, these massacres continued.

The first evening, Mme. Duplay waited in vain for her guest. Though Maximilien had left the Jacobins at the usual hour of adjournment, it was noted that he had not departed alone. A tall and handsome young man accompanied him. He was elegantly dressed in a high stock and top boots; his sandy hair under the broad brim of his soft felt hat framed an almost feminine face. He seemed to be about twenty-five years old. He walked erect, speaking gravely without gestures, with a carriage and bearing which, at his age, created the most bizarre contrast. This young man whose name Paris did not yet know, was Saint Just. At first this strange young man, this Adonis of the Provinces, astonished everyone and placed all on their guard. But the maxims which fell from his beautiful and mournful mouth seemed drawn from the *Dialogue of Eucrate and Sylla* by Montesquieu, a book Maximilien greatly admired. Friendship sprang up very quickly between them. Their impenetrable souls understood each other with so haughty a silence that later on they perished side by side without exchanging a word. . . .

In these execrable days of September, Maximilien became friends with this unknown and sententious young man. Saint Just only remained in Paris over one post. As early as Tuesday he planned to take the diligence from St. Quentin to Noyon, where he would catch the chaise for Blérancourt. He desired the Incorruptible's advice before presenting himself as candidate from Aisne to the Convention.

On this terrible evening, the streets on the right bank were silent and deserted. Many Parisians had passed the day in the country, at Montmartre or Chaillot. Because of the warm weather, few of the theaters were open, and in the cafés and cabarets only occasional drunkards were to be seen. But all the way to the Square of Buci the gutters of rue Bourbon-le-Château ran red with blood. While the light of torches and blazing straw reddened the clouds above the Abbey, while half a mile away a bloodthirsty mob yelled under their cutlasses, the Place Vendôme with its old hotels and gardens, its statues and quiet trees, slumbered in the warm fragrance of a summer night.

Robespierre and Saint Just walked along unhurried.

Street lamps swinging in the night breeze cast lengthening shadows of these two nocturnal figures.

"Where are you stopping?" Maximilien asked.

"Near by," replied Saint Just, "in the little hotel of the Soissonnais."

"I will take you there," Maximilien said politely. "The night is clear. Let us speak of our duties. Our task is a bitter one and harsh. Traitors. . . ."

The two men were swallowed by the darkness of the narrow streets. Still conversing they arrived at the door of the hotel. Maximilien, absorbed by his thoughts and burning with somber fire, accompanied his disciple to his room. At this moment the distant sound of the tocsin entered the open window. Robespierre remained silent. Phlegmatically, Saint Just stretched himself out on the bed.

"Excuse me," he said. "The fatigue of the trip. . . ."

"The tocsin," Robespierre murmured. "Can one think of sleeping on such a night?"

"Bah!" replied the young patriot. "Shall one mitigate the convulsions of a society which struggles between liberty and death? Do I find this weakness in you, Robespierre? Bah! I think I will rise and lead you home. No? It's getting late. . . ."

"Sleeping?" said Maximilien.

He studied the glowing clouds in the distance. Stretched out on the bed, Saint Just closed his eyes and smiled. At once consciousness surrendered; his head, like an archangel's, fell backward on the pillow, and overcome with fatigue, he slept. During all the rest of the night he lay motionless. In the morning when he awoke he saw Robespierre standing before the open window, between the flowered curtains.

"Is that you? And what led you here so early?"

"Do you think that I have returned?" said Robespierre.

Nevertheless he seemed like a man who has been shaken out of a deep sleep and who is cold. He walked across the room and took up his hat.

"No," he said. "I have not left the room. I have not slept. Au revoir, my friend. I hope your fellow-citizens will render justice to your patriotism. Return to us. We need men who are pure."

"Yes," replied Saint Just. "And farewell!"

CHAPTER TWELVE

On the twenty-first of January, 1793, a little before nine o'clock in the morning, mother Duplay at a sign from Maximilien covered up the linen she was bleaching with wood-ashes in the courtyard. After wiping her hands on her apron, she slowly climbed the stairs to the room on the second floor which overlooked Rue Saint-Honoré. There she saw her two daughters seated before a window, scraping linen to make lint for bandages.

"Come downstairs, my dears," said Mme. Duplay. "You can do that as well in the salon as you can here."

Elizabeth and Eléonore looked up with surprise, but as obedient and sensible daughters they followed out their mother's instructions in silence. Having pulled the shutters to, Mme. Duplay herself descended to the court, and continued with her washing. In the workshop the smoothing planes hissed. The air was cold and dry, while slight traces of snow lay on the roofs of houses. From the Tuileries rose the deep sound of thunder.

A man with a wooden leg stumped in through the arch. He was Simon Duplay, discharged volunteer of '92 who had left his leg at Valmy. Nevertheless he still maintained his military bearing and at present worked as carpenter for his uncle with a cockade as big as his fist stuck in his broad-brimmed hat. Limping along he made his way toward the lumber room when a voice he knew well made him raise his head.

"Simon!"

"Yes, it's I."

"I'm coming down," Maximilien called.

The next moment Maximilien was in the small court questioning him.

"Well, what's happening?"

"I've just returned from the boulevards. Paris is under arms. Every window in the city is shut. Cannons loaded with grape shot are trained on every square. The cannoneers have fuses and tinder at hand. By Christ, it's like a great forest of pikes. Everyone must keep quiet. Ah! you don't see something like this every day."

"No," said Robespierre, distantly.

"A courier has gone at full speed to the City Hall. They say Louis is in a green coach, with two gendarmes and his confessor. He wanted Jacques Roux, the Pastor of the Sans-Culottes as they call him, to take charge of his will."

"I know," said Maximilien.

"Roux refused to take it, saying, 'I'm here only to lead you to the scaffold!' "

"The scoundrel! What cowardliness!"

Surprised, the soldier stared at Robespierre. Then, after a moment, he continued.

"Monsieur Capet replied: 'That's true!' Then another officer of the guard accepted the paper."

At these words the street door slammed shut and Duplay appeared. After turning the key, he placed it in his pocket. Mlle. Duplay, who was alarmed and puzzled by all the excitement, came out of the salon.

"Father," she exclaimed, "what's the matter? Why these precautions?"

"Your father is right," said Maximilien. "Something is about to happen which you must not see."

An hour later people returned singing along Rue Saint Honoré, having seen Louis XVI guillotined. A few of the more savage in the mob brandished sabers, whose points were reddened with blood. A crowd of street peddlers, always evident at such times and places, offered little packages of the dead king's hair for sale. Others peddled buttons and pieces of gray cloth they said had been torn from his clothes. In a short while the crowd had melted away.

About noon the news vendors ran through the streets, crying their journals, still damp from the press. Stabled since dawn in their sheds, hacks now began to appear; the bells of garbage men were heard and the cries of chestnut peddlers: "Get them while they're hot, Messieurs!" Knife grinders with their barrows, vinegar merchants, rabbit dealers, chimney sweeps, water carriers, organ grinders. . . . The hubbub of a workaday world filled the streets. In the evening the theaters opened, and under the oil lamps crowds of laughing people waited in line as if nothing extraordinary had taken place that day.

The apathy of the people astonished those at Duplays', but Simon repeated a remark he had overheard:

"A king's head should make no more noise when it falls than the head of any other man."

CHAPTER THIRTEEN

"Do you realize," said I, "that the Convention has been in existence for four months to the very hour?"

"Four months," Maximilien repeated.

He remained silently staring at the fire. Many deputies were present at the Duplays' that evening and all were puzzled by the strange uneasiness which hung over the Convention. It groped its way along, paralyzed by the rivalries of its influential groups. For the most part, the leaders who had learned to handle assemblies studied the lay of the land and eyed one another watchfully. The mass of the delegates had come from the Constituent and Legislative Assemblies. They followed Danton, Vergniaud, or even Marat, for very few of them believed in the future ascendency of Robespierre. The majority thought that his star had already set.

Was it this which embittered him? Who among his colleagues believed in him? Who had a presentiment that one day he was to hold them in his power? The strange blindness that affects Assemblies made it impossible for this one to understand that its designated leader would be a man whom the majority of its members happened to know well.

What was this convention if not a conglomeration of the upper and middle class? On the benches of the Manège there were forty-nine clericals and one blooded prince. The rest were lawyers, doctors, writers, actors, merchants, farmers, bankers. Among the seven hundred and forty-eight votes of seven hundred and forty-eight members, there was one ballot alone which was dropped in the ballot-box by a calloused hand. This one and only proletarian was named Armonville, a wool carder from Rheims, and though he was the only delegate who wore the *bonnet rouge,* he was not numbered among the most honored members. In fact the Convention was made in the image of the Jacobins.

Later on this was to explain not only Maximilien's supremacy, but other questions. At this time, however, the more obvious aspects of the assembly occupied his thoughts. He tried to explain to his own satisfaction the coolness of a legislature into which he had entered triumphantly, having been elected by a larger plurality in Paris than even Danton; having, moreover, led all other candidates in the Pas-de-Calais, thus representing not only the laboring classes but every section in Paris from the faubourgs to the courts.

This unexpected resistance recalled his first entrance into politics. He well understood that once again he must slowly and painfully break down the prejudices of his colleagues; he realized that in this present assembly, as in that of 1789 through which the voice of Mirabeau had thundered, he must battle against another storm—Danton

—and he knew that he would conquer only by the cold, arid, and doctrinaire methods he had used before.

In his very first speech he had, at a glance, gauged his difficulties. Danton, having replied to the attack of Lasource "against the triumvirate of Danton, Robespierre, and Marat," had left the tribune with the gathering clouds of storm above it.

Robespierre, speaking as he had spoken to the Jacobins, surrendered to that tedious weakness of his of enumerating his services to the nation. At Rue Saint Honoré, this type of justification made the audience weep, but the Convention took it ill. His speech was received in deathly silence. Robespierre, goaded by his outraged pride, had, in a tone of vexation, turned to the galleries. There were murmurs against him even there. In short, the whole affair was a rebuff.

One thing, however, saved him. For Barbaroux and Rebecqui rose to describe their visit at Duplays' when the Incorruptible had openly avowed his aspiration to the dictatorship. Maximilien, meanwhile, having taken his seat, allowed Panis to reply, who, as a witness of the interview, gave the lie to the two Marseillais.

Thus the attack dragged on, but it permitted Robespierre to examine his position in an Assembly which he planned to lead in the approaching battle.

What he knew would have discouraged any other man. On one side stood Danton the wrestler, a man of women and of mobs, who seduced both by making them lower their eyes. On the other side stood the Gironde, a scholarly, brilliant, intelligent, brave legion of predominantly wealthy men. As is common among the young, they despised Robespierre as a poor man, a foundation scholar, a needy lawyer, and hated him enviously as the eminent Jacobin, and the foremost delegate of Paris. These on one side and Danton on the other made up the Convention. Robespierre was isolated, reduced to a haughty silence. It was between Danton and the Girondins the battle was to be waged. The Girondins thought only of dragging down Danton, and Maximilien, excluded from the skirmish of September 25, realized that they would even refuse him the bitter tribute of their sarcasm. They prepared, thought he, to let him stumble into the void, unheeded and alone.

His forebodings were unfounded, as we shall see. But whatever they were, he took breath slowly and patiently in order to scale those heights he had lost.

CHAPTER FOURTEEN

Toward the end of October, on the eve of the trial of the King, Maximilien, burning for battle, had found himself overwhelmed. He obtained what he no longer had hoped for—a mass maneuver against him. His popularity was to be tested by the naïvely laid snare of an impromptu debate, concluding with a long speech of indictment which would occupy the entire session and which, if it did not overthrow him, would carry him to the pinnacle of fame.

The occasion arrived on the 29th of October. Maximilien had long awaited it. He was prepared; this plot, hatched in the Salon of Mme. Roland, did not catch him off his guard.

Guadet presided in the chair. The scene had been set in advance as if it were to be presented upon the stage. Lanjuinais opened the first act by reading a report by Roland against the Commune. Robespierre did not find himself directly named, but designated; in veiled words he was accused of conspiring with the cut-throats of the September massacre.

He leaped to the tribune. His enemies awaited him there. They drowned out his voice which had never been powerful and which only by force of will he had strengthened slightly. Guadet, from the chair, did his best to deny Maximilien an opportunity to defend himself. Yet they could not prevent him from making his voice heard and exciting his adversaries.

"There is not a man here who dares accuse me to my face or dares to carry on a serious and calm discussion with me upon this tribune!"

It was then the Gironde removed its mask. A small energetic man slowly climbed to the tribune. It was Louvet again, the intrepid and weak Louvet, the same man whose attack on Robespierre at the Jacobins in 1791 had so disastrously run aground.

His speech, in which he looked forward to revenge, had been prepared months before. He began with the words:

"A great conspiracy threatens to gather over France. . . ."

Louvet spoke for two hours until, carried along by applause, he reached his famous peroration:

"Robespierre, I accuse you. . . ."

Maximilien rose, amid a storm of yells. However, he did not lose his self-assurance.

"I ask," said he, "a delay to examine the charges against me and a day set apart for me to reply to them in a manner which will be as satisfactory as it will be victorious."

"That is just," said Vergniaud.

The fifth of November was agreed upon.

Friends of the Incorruptible trembled for his future. As he remained invisible, entirely occupied by the drawing up of his reply, a rumor spread that a conspiracy against his life had been formed. Every evening a mob flooded Rue Saint Honoré, before the house of Duplay. Nicolas the printer, armed with a cudgel, acted as bodyguard. Precautions were by no means unnecessary, for on November 3, dragoons under orders from the Girondins came in from the provinces. Galloping up and down the boulevards, they flourished their sabers and vomited forth imprecations against the Incorruptible. From time to time they would pull up their horses before a café, where, after chanting a funeral march, they would dash off yelling:

"To the Guillotine, Robespierre!"

Saint Just denounced these actions before the Jacobins, and Augustin Robespierre followed him upon the floor.[1]

On Sunday, November 4, before a few of his friends Maximilien delivered a secret reading of his reply. That night he kept the lamp burning in his room until very late, still polishing his speech, cutting and tightening its phrases. He slept late.

Sometime before noon I went to get him. We took our way toward the Manège attended by the Duplays, Saint Just, and "Bonbon." The session had already been called to order.

[1] He had been at Paris for five weeks, having been elected as a delegate from Paris to the Convention. With Charlotte he lodged in the house of the Duplays in the rooms just over the entry.

CHAPTER FIFTEEN

We entered by the Feuillants' gate. On the other side of the hall the crowd struggled to enter. It was one of those days when the irresistible curiosity of the mob broke down gates and ripped doors from their hinges. The pressure of the mob was so great toward the Terrasse that the National Guards had to join hands in a long chain to hold back the impatient tide of men. In the famous "private passage," decorated with striped ticking, reëchoed cries and oaths. Even in the hall itself the uproar could be heard.

The door we had taken led to the rail, just opposite the platform of the speaker, Héraut de Séchelles. He was called "Handsome Héraut"; and he was in fact the Adonis of an Assembly which was not at all lacking in good-looking men.

Ushers, clothed in black with powdered hair, passed back and forth near the huge faience stove built in reproduction of the Bastille. The minutes were read in a hubbub from all parts of the hall which drowned out the ushers' cries of "Silence, gentlemen! Take your seats." The uproar became deafening when Héraut sounded the bell. The deputies who thronged in the semicircle ran toward their seats.

"The order of the day," shouted the President above the disturbance, "calls for a discussion of Louvet's denunciation. Robespierre, you have the floor."

Maximilien, looking very pale, arose. In the galleries the women applauded. A second stroke of the bell established a profound, an almost oppressive, silence. With one hand thrust into the opening of his vest and the other resting on the balustrade, he slowly and solemnly climbed the steps of the tribune.

"Citzens! Delegates of the people . . . "

The speech lasted three hours. Louvet suffered like a man locked in the pillory. Camille wrote next day in his journal: "Robespierre unloaded fifty tons of manure onto that bald head."

"An accusation, if not formidable, at least very serious, has been lodged against me before the National Convention," Robespierre began. "Of what am I accused? Of having conspired to obtain the dictatorship, or the triumvirate, or the tribuneship. The opinions of my adversaries do not seem entirely certain on the exact word. Let us, therefore, translate all these slightly conflicting Latin expressions into the phrase 'Supreme Power,' which my accuser has employed elsewhere."

After this introduction, he took up one by one all the grievances Louvet had set forth. He explained his interview with Marat, his rôle in the Jacobin Club and in the Commune, his part in the uprising of August 10. He came finally to the prison massacres.

"If you have believed," said he, "that the spirit impressed upon the people's minds by the insurrection of August had entirely disappeared in the first weeks of September, you have deceived yourselves; and those who have sought to persuade you that there is no relation between the one and the other of these two uprisings have failed to understand not only the facts but the human heart also."

Then in a low, almost indistinct voice which veiled his pain in describing them, he outlined the story of those terrible days of blood. The audience, lulled by this mournful threnody, suddenly saw Maximilien shift to his attack. It was brief and mordant.

"M. Louvet," he exclaimed, raising his voice, "began one of his articles in the *Sentinelle* with these words: 'All honor to the General Council of the Commune! It sounded the tocsin, it has saved the country!' "

And Robespierre, ignoring the muttering of the crowd, turned a withering glance upon Louvet and added:

"It was at the time of the elections."

With this statement, he seized the whip.

"Citizens! If ever, following the example of the Lacedemonians, we raise a temple to Fear, I suggest that its priests be chosen from those men who ceaselessly babble about their courage and the perils they face for us."

Then he pounced upon Roland:

"O virtuous man, exclusively and eternally virtuous, whither do you wish to go along these shadowy ways? The next time examine more carefully the instruments that are placed in your hands!"

At this moment a deep roar of voices filled the hall. With a deliberate and dispassionate gesture Maximilien placed a page of his speech on the table before him, paused and then read that section which opened the floodgates of merciless war.

"You will one day know what price you should affix to the moderation of that man whom you wish to ruin. And do you believe that if I wished to lower myself to similar accusations, it would be difficult for me to offer you more definite and more firmly supported indictments? However, I have never believed in the courage of the wicked. But consider your own acts and see with what clumsiness you have fallen into your own traps. For a long time you have tried to force the Assembly into passing a law against instigators to murder. If it is passed, who will be the first victim it must strike?"

A shudder passed through the Assembly. These words, whose tragic import no man could yet gauge, stirred the members deeply. A conciliatory peroration, whose sincerity was rendered dubious by the pompous eloquence which clothed it, did not temper the effect of these threats.

Robespierre left the tribune to the cheers of the public. A printing of the speech was voted, in spite of the furious resistance of Barbaroux who, seeing himself refused the floor, ran to the rail crying:

"You will hear me, or I will hew my denunciation in stone."

There was laughter, but Barère, whom Maximilien

dubbed "The Equivocator," obtained the floor. It was to deliver an insolent defense of the Incorruptible.

"Let us not erect," said he, "pedestals for pigmies!"

And he justified the order of the day.

"Keep your order of the day," said Robespierre, cuttingly. "I do not wish it if it contains a preamble injurious to me."

The Convention voted the order of the day unconditionally. Robespierre had won.

But the mortal struggle between these men had only just commenced. Unknowingly they drifted toward internecine slaughter. Batch by batch at sinister and regular intervals, until the fiery night of Thermidor, they descended headless to the tomb. Vergniaud had a foreboding of this fate, when he exclaimed:

"The Revolution, like Saturn, devours its children!"

CHAPTER SIXTEEN

About this time the city became curious about the Duplays. These evenings on Rue Saint Honoré supplied just the food Parisian small talk flourished on. For though the Revolution had set the head of a king on the frontiers of the country like a boundary-stone, it had nevertheless imposed neither silence nor respect on these, the most indiscreet citizens of the world. In fact, Paris was as garrulous and malicious as ever.

Concerning the Duplays there were as many opinions as there were tongues to express them. The political salons, and in particular that of Mme. Roland, railed violently against the salon of Mme. Duplay, while the Jacobins and the working class never mentioned it except sympathetically. At the Convention, busybodies and the knowing displayed uneasiness; the humble and unsociable retreat of the Incorruptible led them to believe that he was sequestered to the profit of some scheming cabal. Danton laughed, he ridiculed his rival—"all surrounded," said he, "with louts and beldames." And the Gironde laughed with him, while Maximilien coldly watched them laugh.

However, the evenings on Rue Saint Honoré were no longer like those I had attended in 1791 when I first arrived in Paris. Their intimacy, which I had found so attractive then, had been supplanted by an austere pomposity. It was a Jacobin clique—in many ways a kind of grand council of Robespierrism.

Saint Just was an assiduous member, with Couthon and Lebas. Fouché, David, Prudhon, Merlin (de Thionville), Collot d'Herbois, La Réveillère-Lepeaux, were also frequently seen there.

After a rather lively attack upon him, Pétion had not appeared since September; and at any rate he had begun to incline toward the Gironde. If my memory is correct it was in the month of January, 1793, that M. Buonarotti,[1] the descendant of Michel Angelo, appeared among us for the first time. He was a musician. Many times thereafter he sang the songs of Mehul and Gossec for us, in his warm and sonorous Italian voice, while Eléonore accompanied him on the harpsichord. There was another Italian, the decorator Cietti, and the Corsican Galandini, who, faithful and violent like all his race, assuming the position of Robespierre's bodyguard, would have cut the throats of half the Convention to defend him. I remember also the Lyonnais Gravier, a locksmith from Choisy, and Lohier the grocer. From time to time Camille Desmoulins still appeared. But Danton often led him away to the wine cellars of the Palais-Royal, for Camille no longer felt himself in sympathy with these austere conventicles the cabinetmaker held with so much pride.

As to Mme. Duplay, the good woman surrounded Maxi-

[1] M. Buonarotti now lives an exile in Bruxelles. 1825.

milien with every care. Never was a guest more pampered. She guarded him with so jealous an affection that it led to an unfortunate affair I must describe.

To begin with, it must be remembered that since the opening of the Convention, Augustin, as an elected delegate, had taken up his residence in Paris. Mlle. Robespierre accompanied him. On leaving Arras, they had leased their house on Rue Rats-Porteurs.

The cabinetmaker, who was hospitality itself, and who in addition to Maximilien and old Anthoine, already lodged his brave nephew Simon (who was known in that part of the city as Duplay-Wooden-Leg), now offered rooms to Charlotte and Bonbon. They accepted an apartment above the entrance, with windows overlooking Rue Saint Honoré. Now these rooms, the best in the whole house, did not communicate with Maximilien's garret, which was situated in a wing between Simon's and that of M. and Mme. Duplay. Thus Charlotte could not do her brother's housekeeping, which still remained in the hands of Mme. Duplay.

Mlle. Robespierre could not tolerate for long what she considered an infringement on her prerogatives. Had she not for six years at Arras been the vigilant guardian of Maximilien's hearth? Why was her brother in the home of strangers? Moreover, was this garret room over a lumber shed the proper place for a man in Maximilien's position? From the point of view of her provincial respectability, Mlle. Robespierre desired a decent apartment, a salon, and servants for her famous and powerful brother.

But above everything, Mme. Duplay's influence over her brother wounded her to the quick.

It was to me that she first expressed her complaint.

"She monopolizes him," she said. "She wishes to estrange him from me, and he permits himself to be hoodwinked. He, a man of tremendous energy, has nevertheless absolutely no will of his own."

Then, giving way to an irritation which each day increased, she exclaimed:

"What is the matter with him? How can this influence of Mme. Duplay be explained? It is not based on intelligence, you may be sure, for Maximilien has certainly a great deal more than she."

Then on Rue Saint Honoré a battle like that between a priest's maid and his sister started between Charlotte and Maximilien's future mother-in-law. It was a battle of smiles, of daggers, and of honeyed treachery. Good-hearted Duplay tried in vain to restore peace. Eléonore took her mother's side. Elizabeth, who was sweet-tempered and shy, dried the tears of all, while Bonbon tried to disarm everyone with his light-heartedness.

It was trouble wasted, for relations grew more and more bitter. Charlotte Robespierre finally established her brother in a house completely modeled after that of the old one in Arras. As surprising as this appears, it displays Robespierre in his true light for, under the rigid shell of the patriot, there lurked the bourgeois, the man of set habits and the fireside, obedient to all the domestic tyrannies, a retiring homebody, whose heart was easily softened by small attentions and who would never have dared even to scold a servant.

He had surrendered suddenly. Mlle. Robespierre rented an apartment in rue Saint Florentin, and there triumphantly installed her brother. I leave the reader to imagine how, from one end of Paris to the other, and at a time when private life was, so to speak, abolished, this rearrangement was talked about.

Charlotte's victory, however, was brief. No sooner had Maximilien been installed in Rue Saint Florentin than he fell ill. The first visitor who came to see him was Mme. Duplay, who raised her voice in violent protests. A veritable quarrel of old shrews took place, and Mme. Duplay won. Robespierre moved back to his garret.

He was right in doing so. Better than anyone, he understood how much this humble lodging increased his popularity. But Mlle. Robespierre, who really did not know him, could never console herself. She swallowed her anger, even keeping silent on that day when Mme. Duplay returned a jar of preserves to her, saying to the messenger:

"Take it back. I don't wish her to poison the Incorruptible!"

Such was the quarrel. Thanks to Robespierre the Younger, who had the best heart in the world, all public scandal was avoided. In fact, Augustin, profiting by a mission which sent him to the Midi, took his sister along with him and Maximilien again found at Rue Saint Honoré that peace he loved and which subsequent events rendered so necessary to him.

CHAPTER SEVENTEEN

My object is not to describe here all the events to which fate made me a witness. To write the history of the Revolution is entirely beyond my intention and my range. Moreover, no incident, great and terrible as it might be, should usurp the place in my memoirs of the smallest recollection, if that recollection casts light upon the personality of my friend.

Shall I, before and after so many others, make comment upon those days between the death of the king and June 2, 1793, when the fall of the Gironde was impending? Those days will find more gifted writers to describe them. Politics is not my business and at present impartiality would find no refuge in my heart.

Nevertheless I must say that Robespierre, overthrowing the Gironde and sacrificing those great men who composed it, performed a cruel duty. I know that he suffered in doing it. Camille Desmoulins' confession of pity: "Unhappy wretches! It is I who killed them," Robespierre himself stifled in his heart. He was good, I swear it. But his patriotism closed his heart to mercy. Alas! to judge these things today, outside their time and their circumstance, is to judge them badly. One too often forgets that in this struggle wherein they fell the Girondins were often the aggressors.

Since the opening of the Convention, in those days of intoxication which followed the proclamation of the Republic, did they not refuse to grasp those friendly hands which were held out to them? They were drunk with their youth and power, incapable of containing themselves, incapable even of hearing the grave voice of their leader, Vergniaud, who was all sense and good judgment.

Though only a scoundrel would refuse to weep for their death, yet if they had been successful the nation might have been lost. The people themselves realized it, for when they arose to enforce the proscription of the Twenty-two upon the Convention, they acted not from hate, but in defense of two words which had just been given them: "Public Safety." The defeat of the Girondins was, to speak properly, a victory of the workers (that is to say the Commune) over the provinces (that is to say, the Convention).

What is understood less frequently is that the Commune died by the same hand which killed the Gironde—the hand of Robespierre. The Commune, which had been dominated by men of violence and which ever since September received its orders from the club of the *Évêché,* the terrible Commune of '93, was, during the suppression of the Gironde, subjugated by Robespierre.

It is certain that the defeat of the Girondins caused the fall of the Commune. The Gironde dragged the extremists to the scaffold; the extremists perished through the death of moderation. But had Robespierre not been influenced by temporary circumstances, Hébert and his followers would have been the only ones to carry their heads to Sanson.[1] For Robespierre, who did not desire the death of the Girondins and who at first consented to it against his heart, was one day to demand that the ringleaders at City Hall be crushed without pity. Never did he cease to believe that the true enemies of the Republic were demagogues.

At this time the extremists, believing themselves to be masters of the situation, thought only of slaughtering the Girondins. They held their secret meeting in the café Corozza in the Palais Royal, with Tallien and Collot present. Nothing was discussed except throat cutting.

When their threats became more definite a shadowy individual wearing a long gray overcoat came skulking in along the wall.

"Good day, Hard-hitter," said the others as if they were waiting for him.

It was Maillard. He reappeared on the 10th of March for the insurrection which had been abandoned on account of rain. He had not been seen again since September. Learning there was no need of him this time, he had plunged back into the shadows to appear punctually and dismally on the night of the 27th of June, when Marinot,

[1] Charles Henri Sanson, the executioner from 1788-95, was one of the famous family who had practiced their profession of head-chopping from 1688. His son, the last of the line, was executioner until he died in 1840. During the Terror the elder Sanson called in several of his brothers to help him out in the provinces. *Tr.*

the painter on porcelain, made a proposition at the *Évêché*. He suggested that the twenty-two Girondins be seized in their beds and that they be spirited off to a house in the faubourg Saint Jacques where they could be quietly put out of the way. Twenty-two graves, dug in advance, would receive their bodies. On the next day the news would be circulated that they had fled the country. But another of the group, a police official, declared that there was no house whose walls were thick enough to smother their cries. The miniaturist's attractive idea must for that reason be abandoned. Shaking his head so that his copper earrings danced, Maillard, with his hat pulled down over his eyes, retired as he had come.

Meanwhile the Gironde continued to pile up mistakes. Its leaders, preventing Cambon from saving the country's finances, attempted to fill the depleted coffers of the state with their own golden harangues. Indeed, they, the fathers of the Republic, even allowed themselves to be compromised by the Royalists! They became more and more moderate and went from one imprudence to another. The Commission of Twelve, which offered M. Barère [1] to them as a safe pilot, immediately ran their ship onto the rocks and they were unable to find a way of getting rid of him. But even this was not enough; they abolished parliamentary immunity from arrest. And why? To send Marat

[1] M. Barère de Vieuzac, who is now exiled as a regicide, lives, it is said, in Brussels. But the miseries of his exile should not allow people to forget his treachery toward all parties which brought upon him the name of "The Anacreon of the Guillotine."

before the revolutionary tribunal, whence he returned in triumph on the shoulders of workmen.

But they must, forsooth, do even more than this to ruin themselves; they delivered speeches of incomprehensible folly. First Guadet, a clever and honest man, but one easily blinded by anger, spoke of breaking down the authority of Paris. This gave M. Isnard a chance to utter his immortal though suicidal phrase:

"I declare it to you, Paris will be annihilated, and soon one will search along the banks of the Seine to see if Paris ever existed!"

To what giddiness did these great men succumb? They saw death approaching and seemed to call out for it to make haste. Had not Vergniaud said as much when he refused to convoke the primary assembly? Perish the Gironde! In reality the Girondins committed suicide.

Paris was outraged. The mad provocations of Isnard inflamed the least hot-tempered. The most decrepit home-bodies, the hoariest men of law, shopkeepers, skittle-bowlers, snuff-merchants, a thousand and one honest fellows whom four years of civil strife had not shaken loose from their set habits, now spoke of rushing to arms. They even talked of impaling all the Girondins on pikes, so greatly had the apostrophe of Isnard enraged them.

Meanwhile suspicious-looking men, whose vests displayed as many pistols as there were pockets, roamed through the cafés starting arguments and then disappearing. The atmosphere of another First of September hung over the faubourgs. One cannot describe the picture of this political, gallant, sword-forging Paris of '93 which made arms and love while reading newspapers. It was a great Bacchic period in which men like Robespierre were strong through their sobriety. Everyone lived in the streets and the cafés, where patriots drank Suresnes wine served in tricolored pitchers by former nobles, while old aristocrats, scorned and ridiculed, tossed griddle cakes and fritters under the porches of their old hotels. And how many itinerant trades there were, even to the trade of orator which Varlet practiced as vinegar peddler. Bread was lacking, but never were so many useless articles of luxury purchased. Women dressed in striped cretonnes thought only of perfume; hair-dressing parlors were crowded with coquettes in wooden shoes, and Paris ceased to sing only to work itself into a "buggerly rage" over the Girondins.

CHAPTER EIGHTEEN

Some months before I had changed my lodging place, not only to escape the importunities of my brother, but also to comply with the necessities of my occupation, which I will mention. Moving out of the Hotel de Consuls, I rented two attic rooms of a narrow house overlooking Rue Saint Honoré.

By leaning out the window a little I could see all the street from the Feuillants to the Oratoire. I scarcely thought, when I first moved in, that I had hired a box in the theater of death. However, that is what happened.

The Revolutionary Tribunal had just been instituted, and all the condemned filed by under my windows. They went and returned, they passed below my windows twice; first as they moved toward the *quais des Mofondus* and the guillotine; the second time when, lifeless, they passed along those façades their eyes had watched avidly, before closing forever in eternal darkness. The tumbrils dripped blood as they lurched over the cobblestones, bearing their headless burdens to the cemetery of Rue Pigalle or Sainte Marguerite.

This lasted for more than a year, until the Commune

decided to perform the executions at the Place du Trône.[1]

What memories filed past below my windows! I saw Charlotte Corday in her scarlet chemise, then Adam Lux who died for love of her. I saw the Queen wearing her little cap, preceded by a mounted official of the municipality, who, like a toy, raised and lowered his sword to command silence. I saw General Custines with his bald head and stooped shoulders, so valiant under fire, but under the hoots and laughter of the mob weeping into his great mustache. I saw Philippe Egalité, who died like a king.

The same roar always announced the approach of the cortège. First came the shrill screams and laughter of women which, breaking off now and again into silence, permitted one to hear the "Gee! Whoa" of the cart drivers, the beat of horses' hoofs, or the rattle of sabers. The jostling tumbrils proceeded slowly. The condemned, bound to the wagon sides, their heads bare, shirts open, stood or sat with their backs turned to the horses. Some of them lowered their heads, others prayed, many laughed back at the insults hurled at them by the crowd, others studied the street with deep interest. But cowards were rare; the larger part of them bore up bravely, not only from pride but for the glory of their names.

At first these mournful cavalcades attracted throngs of the curious. But little by little, because the same thing was to be seen each day, the people no longer took notice of them. Men would even pass through the cortège to

[1] Now the Place de la Nation. *Tr.*

proceed toward their business. It was at this time that Sanson obtained permission from the Commune to cease dismantling the scaffold after every execution.

One day something other than the usual cries were heard. It was a song. Twenty voices were singing the Hymn of the Marseillais.[2] The refrain which reëchoed through the street gripped the paid rioters with such power that they remained speechless, no longer daring to ply their brutal trade. Five tumbrils wound through the streets and on these tumbrils the Girondins, their heads and breasts bare, sang with full throats.

At times from a window or a spur-post some enraged *sans-culotte* would yell:

"Vive la République!"

And the Girondins, ceasing for a moment to sing, would shout back:

"Vive la République!"

Vergniaud was in the fourth tumbril. His hands were bound, his hair was matted to his head with rain, while an old coat was slung across his shoulders by its sleeves. Everyone recognized his face, with its broad forehead, its firm mouth, its tender eyes. The people heard his voice in silence, they heard it singing strong and unfalteringly, singing still when the great man, his feet damp with the pure blood of his comrades, watched the cruel triangle fall nineteen times before he himself was placed beneath it.

[2] Though twenty-one Girondins had been condemned, one of them had committed suicide in prison. His corpse was dragged to the guillotine in one of the tumbrils and beheaded as a matter of form. *Tr.*

EXECUTION OF THE GIRONDINS.

When they had passed, windows were closed, hacks and passers-by scurried through the rain. Each man returned to his work. What gives this age its atrocious grandeur is certainly the fact that one could witness such a sight with dry eyes. Things become common more quickly than one believes; the sublime happens but once. Like all the rest of mankind, the most sensitive of beings ended by finding natural what occurred every day.

I thought of this one cold morning in October, 1793, while putting on my cloak before going outdoors. Indeed (and it is still a sign of these times), if the sublime horror attending the death of the Girondins only feebly stirred the people, certain men, of whom I was one, were dismayed by the circumstances surrounding their trial. It is known that it was cut short by a decree of the Convention, which permitted the jury to conclude the trial "if it declared itself sufficiently enlightened." The cowardly jury obeyed. Thus in contempt of all justice, in contempt of all legal usage, they applied new laws to a trial begun under a different judiciary code.

As a man of law, an attorney and a judge, I had and still have today, a deep aversion toward all illegality. Moreover, I believed the Revolution should not return to the most deadly of all past abuses, after having sealed its charter of human rights with so much blood. These thoughts rose in my mind, as with hurried steps I made my way toward the Château where my duties called me before ten o'clock.

Here, perhaps, is the proper moment for me to speak of

the unexpected change in my state of affairs. For two months I had been connected with the office of the Committee of Public Safety. Maximilien had called me there a short while after becoming a member of the Committee during the end of July.

Some weeks before that I had lost the position as assistant judge in the criminal court. But Robespierre's friendship was forthcoming, and I had accepted a position in which I could find proper employment for my talents. It was that of chief clerk in the bureau for the surveillance of the execution of law.

Here I met in these rooms, which had formerly been those of Marie Antoinette, illustrious men intermingled with the lowest scoundrels. In the office of the Committee I had many scholars and jurists as chiefs and colleagues.[1]

There were also visitors. In fact it was a continuous and half-monstrous sideshow.

If some day I undertake to tell all that I saw and heard there . . . But no. There are secrets an honest man knows how to keep. As a report of what happened during those terrible sessions one will never have more than the official list of arrests. That is to say, nothing. At least it is known what happened in the anteroom. It was there I met every type a country in convulsion could produce of sharpers, spies, profiteers, conspirators, free-lance brokers, libelers, secret agents, money-making priests, veiled women, interlopers, grafting deputies, fat trades-

[1] Certain men living today have gone too far along the road of success to remember their passage through the Revolution with pleasure.

men, over-wealthy strangers. . . . A squalid and restless police haunted the corridors. Through them I learned everything. Through them I saw the underworld and the sub-underworld of the revolution. I saw brothels and the offices of stock-jobbers; through them I learned of my brother's arrest, for a dishonest carting business he had operated with the Abbé of Epagnac. I learned of his escape and flight.

I knew all. I should have preferred not to have known what I learned on the 31st of October, the morning after the death of the twenty Girondins, who, as the victims of an illegal decree, I considered to have received an unfair trial. Now this decree through my official position came into my hands that very morning. I looked at it and turned pale. It was in Robespierre's handwriting

CHAPTER NINETEEN

My duties having ended, I hurried away to see Maximilien. I often surprised him at this hour, which he usually passed in rest or reading. I found him alone completing his toilet. He received me with his usual friendliness, as if he found my visit a diversion from his work. We rarely spoke of politics, but rather of our memories.

Maximilien, observing the altered expression of my face, seemed disturbed by it.

"What has happened?" he asked.

Without further ado I told him my thoughts, the sorrow I felt at seeing my friend, the companion of my youth, the man whose talents and virtue I so much admired, abandoning himself to certain actions. I searched for words; I hesitated, finally gaining courage I spoke of the decree. I spoke of it firmly in a tone which masked my sorrow.

Never will I forget what followed. In its slightest details I recall the scene. Maximilien sat opposite me, a dressing gown flung across his shoulders. He listened to me without flinching. But placing the paper knife he was holding on the table, he turned upon me a glance which had suddenly become impenetrable.

The expression of this face! One could distinguish no sign of sentiment or feeling upon it. It was the terrible expression which appeared during those rare periods of anger, when he summoned all his powers to restrain himself. It was an expression whose impassibility neither the marble faces of statues nor the faces of the shrouded dead could display. He stared at me fixedly; and I bore his eyes without lowering mine. Finally he spoke.

"Oh, well," said he icily. "And what then?"

"You will," said I without raising my voice, "go from illegality to illegality. Take care. I speak to you as a free citizen, as I have always done. Maximilien, you have surrendered to your own enemies and to the enemies of your country. This decree is not your work, it is the work of Hébert and Chaumette."

Robespierre, who until then had remained seated, his legs crossed beneath his bathrobe, leaped to his feet and took a step toward me. But without wavering, I continued.

"I know what it has cost you to hear that. But if others displayed more courage, I might be able to display less bluntness."

"Continue," said he.

"Very well. It is the scoundrels in City Hall who have taken advantage of you in this business. Who ran to the Jacobins the day before yesterday and persuaded them to introduce the motion to the Assembly, if it was not Hébert? Yes, it is they and they alone who bully the deputies into a betrayal of law!"

Anger overcame me, as it overcame Maximilien who interrupted violently.

"The law has not been violated! The Convention is master of its own decrees."

"What mockery! How can you assert that, when the decree was passed under the intimidations of the clubs."

"And even so, does that prove the decree does not respect legal guarantees?"

"Which? Article 14 of the Constitution?" [1]

"Sophistry!"

"Indeed?"

Robespierre shrugged his shoulders and reseated himself. In the silence, he began drumming on the table as he always did in his moments of trouble or suspicion. He could not doubt that I was right, for as a lawyer he himself had too great a respect for law to despise it. But without stumbling over the obstacle, he continued.

"The Convention as well as the people's societies have passed upon it. Why, then, is the argument prolonged? But if the advice of certain people had been listened to, there would have been no trial. I have done my best to avoid extreme measures. I have saved what I could. The seventy-three owe me their lives."

"You had another duty—that of fighting the decree. But on the contrary it was you who desired it."

He stared at me fixedly.

[1] "No one shall be tried except under a law promulgated prior to the offense."

"Yes," I continued. "You drew it up yourself. It is in your own minute handwriting."

I looked at him in silence. He understood.

"Well," said he. "And what are you driving at?"

Leaning with one elbow on the table, he studied me with such deep suspicion that my face flushed.

"Maximilien. I dare in my own turn to ask you a question. Speak your mind. Can you believe that your friend . . ."

I had crossed my arms, and with face thrust forward I almost shouted the words.

"I believe nothing," he said in a voice of ice. "I am not even angry. I respect the immunity of a friend who is deluded."

My face grew even redder.

"No, Maximilien, no! I refuse that offensive prerogative. Is not my action the guarantee of my loyalty? I speak here not only as a friend, but as a citizen. If it is true that thirty years of devoted friendship give me some advantage, today I do not wish to thank it for your indulgence in listening to me. And now you are at liberty to banish an over-sincere friend who does not know how to disguise his convictions."

I must say that Maximilien no longer hesitated. He came over to me very much moved, and held out his hand.

"It is possible that you have expressed yourself too extremely," he murmured. "But I do not doubt either the sincerity of your friendship or of your intentions."

In this remark I saw that his flatterers had not completed

their deadly work. My friend knew how to control himself when he was contradicted or even offended. I did not wish to remain slow in reconciliation. I seized his hand, I pressed it, too affected myself to continue the interview. But he forced me to take a chair. Then in his bare and austere room, the man who made the Convention, the Committees and Generals tremble, opened up his heart to the friend of his lean years. He told me that the illegality of the measures taken against the Gironde was repugnant to him, but that in any way possible the twenty-one had to perish. Indeed he had hoped that certain of them who had been his implacable adversaries would escape with imprisonment.

"Who knows if one day I will not repent having wrested the seventy-three from death. For the others, I bear no hate against them, I swear it. Ah! how much have they required of me! I have desired peace and the safety of my country."

His voice remained for a moment as if suspended. A song rose from the carpenter shop below.

Robespierre then spoke to me of Hébert and his crew. He spoke of them with passion. He did not doubt for an instant that they were traitors under orders from foreign conspirators. To his mind, Gusman, Cauli, and Pio edited *Le Père Duchesne,* not to mention the other royalists who had their men at the Êvêché. The proof? It would be seen shortly. But meanwhile he must be politic, that is to say, patient and prudent, striking only when he was certain to kill, not timidly or feebly attacking these men who were still listened to by the workers and whose victory would be a mortal blow to the Republic.

I listened to my friend. I marveled that, in his passion for public safety, he had forgotten the offense I had given him. And in my happiness at having regained his confidence, I believed that nothing in the future would separate us.

Maximilien accompanied me to the head of the stairs. From the step he gave me his hand. In the crude daylight I saw his face was lined with weariness.

"I am very tired," he said. "I am sick and never was the country confronted by greater dangers. My friend, there are things and reasons that I cannot yet tell you. But are you not one who can understand that silence is often the most sacred obligation? Go, my heart has not changed. Adieu."

Thoughtful and disturbed I wandered off toward my room. Never had the singularity of my position been so vividly revealed. As a friend of a feared and powerful man, of one who in the future was to be regarded as the leader of the Republic, I was, among all his followers, the only one who did not blindly approve of him. As the playfellow of his youth, as a confident of his earliest thoughts, I believed that I could serve him with a disinterest which his flatterers could not destroy. Was he himself aware of it? Alas! What man can call himself strong enough to resist the intoxication of his own triumph?

Perhaps in speaking to him without evasions, as I had done ever since we had studied together at Arras, I had been imprudent. However, doubts weighed on my heart like lead, and it was better that I speak about them in private, than to have made a public quarrel.

I pondered on all this as I walked along Rue Saint Honoré. The weather was damp and cold, while a brisk wind chilled me to the bone. The idea of returning alone to my dark and solitary room seemed too desolate and I went to the Republic Theatre, where "Epicharis and Nero, or The Conspiracy for Freedom" was being performed.

CHAPTER TWENTY

FROM this day of the 24th Ventose 1794, during one hundred and fifteen days Maximilien Robespierre played and won the most arid game of chess a statesman had ever conducted.

The youth of today may try in vain to imagine these feverish months. To visualize the scene they not only lack that passion which consumed us, but also the knowledge of the true rulers of the public during these days which have since been called "The Dog Days" and which opened the Terror.

As a matter of fact there were four powers: The Committee, the Convention, the Commune, and the Jacobins; which four powers superficially represented Force, Law, the People, and Doctrine. Looked at more closely, the divisions were not so clean cut; for above all it was a struggle for influence. The Decemvirate, the Assembly, the City Hall, the Club, were ceaselessly animated by a savage life. Sometimes uniting, sometimes devouring each other, involving and proscribing, banishing their associates, they provoked and terrified each other. Those who ruled one day found themselves overthrown the next. For example: the Jacobins with their innumerable petitions appeared to lead all. But even those members whom they sent before the Assembly often accomplished the will of a rival club, the Cordeliers or the Évêché, who were both allied to the Commune, so that these petitioners, speaking in the name of the Robespierrists, were often as not enemies of the Incorruptible.

Indeed nothing seemed to counterbalance the influence of the Jacobins when, on the 18th of November, Maximilien put through a law which subordinated everything to the decisions of the committees, even the representatives on mission. Already it was protested as a return to royalty when three days later Maximilien restored the Jacobins to all their former power and prestige. But at the same time he eulogized the Convention as a "political and popular body" though ending his speech with a threat against the municipal officers, a threat which Hébert and his crew of enraged followers certainly heard and understood.

At the Convention Robespierre persistently fought the motions of the Commune. He seemed indefatigable. What is more, everyone was astonished to see a man who was so often charged with rigidity maneuver with such subtle tactics as to demand even inconsistency among his followers. Throwing himself from the left side to the right, from terror to clemency, Robespierre in tacking back and forth in this way seemed to have lost all sense of direction. In reality, however, he was progressing toward an end; with a sure foot he climbed a winding road. This course in a broken line was to lead him to the crossroads of the four powers, after he had destroyed that group which still dared to resist him; the Commune.

But over everything and everybody reigned a sovereign power, the Revolutionary Tribunal. Since autumn it belonged to the Incorruptible, who had peopled it with his own men. Fouquier-Tinville alone was his enemy. This jury over which Herman and Dumas presided, Robespierrists to the bitter end, included Payan, Coffinhal, Topino-Lebrun who were all members of the salon Duplay. And Duplay himself. In fact Robespierre held Revolutionary justice in his hand. Each office in the state came under its jurisdiction and looked to it for orders. The Convention guillotined and was guillotined, even as the Sections [1] and the Club. The Committees' turn was to come.

The marvel was that Robespierre, maneuvering between these forces, acting alone among so many different kinds of men, having only his spotless life, a doctrinaire eloquence, and a feeble voice to serve him, succeeded in conquering them all, one after the other. At a time in which distrust and rivalry made the control of the groups the true revolutionary credo, he won that incredible stake: the concentration of power.

When Maximilien broached the struggle, he had only the Jacobins for support, that old force of 1789 which had never betrayed him. At that time the Committees

[1] *Les Sections Parisiennes* were organized in 1790 by the Constituent Assembly. They were composed of Frenchmen who paid a contribution to the government of three days' work. They often influenced the decisions of the Convention. Becoming extreme Jacobins they armed themselves and enforced the accusations against the Girondins. *Tr.*

still acted together. The Convention escaped him. The Commune ruled the Sections, the press, Ministers, representatives attached to the army. The Commune influenced the Jacobins, dominated the Cordeliers, absorbed the Évêché. Even by its excesses it subjugated the Sans-Culottes. It controlled the military. It can be considered the mistress of Paris and the Revolution.

One cannot describe the men who composed it without blushing for humanity. Men of blood and ordure, they aroused hatred of the Revolution with a skill and constancy which, certainly, justified all the suspicions the Incorruptible bore toward them. They invoked Marat, whom death had sanctified. To better deceive the people they shared his old clothes of *l'Ami du Peuple*. They even plagiarized from his journal. Jacques Roux, the "pastor of the Sans-Culottes" had been obliged to reply to this charge of pirating; [1] brought before the criminal court, he stabbed himself. They made another Saint of him. But like Marat, he was exceeded and despised by his fanatic imitators. Thus does violence punish its demagogues. Ronsin blustering with his epaulettes through the cafés shouted that Henriot was a fop and a blackguard, but even he got beyond his depths in his admiration of the mob.

Armonville, nicknamed Bonnet Rouge, despised Ronsin. Gusman, called Tocsinos, despised Armonville. Arthur, the Heart-Eater, despised Gusman. Maillard, the Hard-

[1] Jacques Roux published "L'Ombre de Marat" and was prosecuted by Marat's widow for plagiary. A trumped-up charge of embezzlement was also brought against him. *Tr.*

Hitter, despised Arthur. Fournier, the American, despised Maillard. Dobsent, the Black Eye, despised Fournier. Varlet, the Stirrer of Paris Mud, despised Dobsent. Marino called Greasy Hat, despised Varlet. Charlat, the meat dresser, despised Marino. And Guffroy, called Rougyff, despised them all. It was like a flight of stairs leading to a sewer, on each step of which stood a scoundrel who, raising his eyes, accused his neighbor of being too formal, too much of a "shopkeeper in the merchandise of law."

This whole attitude can be summed up in one word: Hébert, Hébert, the ticket gatherer of the Théatre des Variétés. He had grown rich selling a newspaper edited by another, a poor devil of a libeler named Marquet. For Hébert did not write. *Le Père Duchesne* was an easy master and a poor payer. At the time when the gang entered the Ministry of War, certain editions of it had attained a circulation of six hundred thousand! Assuming the task of persecuting their opponents, the Commune circulated its journal of philippics and curses among the soldiers. Every day, Hébert, dressed like a banker, rolled around in his coach and made merry. But at night before the Cordeliers, he took up the *bonnet rouge* and the language of a "stove merchant." Then he spoke with so revolting a fury that he would make the blackest demagogues recoil. He was like an erupting sewer.

Hébertism was everywhere. A communal tree, its roots lay within the Évêché, but its branches, little by little spread over all the Revolution. Through Vincent it penetrated into the War Office, through Ronsin into the

Army, through Collot d'Herbois into the Committee, through Beurrque into the Jacobins of the Provinces, through Fouché and Carrier into the Delegates on Mission, through Momoro into the Departments. But its real life was in the Commune.

It is a strange thing that the career of the Incorruptible as a statesman was continually tied up with the vicissitudes of the three Communes. The Commune of August 10th placed the Convention under his power. That of 1793 perished by his hand. That of 1794 died with him. The battle in which he was to engage cost him much, and only disgust finally brought him to a decision. What revolted in him above all was his deism and his faith, that deep inner consciousness of a man who even in the worst of the tempest never sloughed off the cassock of a choir boy of Saint-Waast; who spoke of Providence to the Jacobins; who supported Father Gregory against Gobel; who proclaimed the rights of man "in the presence of the Supreme Being"; who invoked heavenly vengeance upon conspirators; who suspected atheists of aristocracy and who, to sum up, remembered having prayed at mass.

It was the Hébertist Commune which gave the signal for sacrilege. It began with the vile Saturnalias of November, with the processions of asses garbed in priests' vestments, with the drunken riots of Saint Eustache, with the profanation of the tabernacles, with the trousers of purple velvet cut from ecclesiastical robes. These acts of profanation, cried up by Hébert's clique (which they disavowed like cowards the following week) had only one purpose: to dishonor the Revolution by arousing decency and religious faith against it.

They placed their money on the winning card, that of Sans-Culottism. They howled at the moderates so furiously and so constantly, that to oppose their attacks finally amounted to a confession of being lukewarm. This forced them back onto their own tracks and they ended by shuddering at not appearing cannibalistic enough. O misery of pride!

During the celebration of the 2nd Pluviose, they considered it piquant to compare the National Legislature and the hangman, by marking out the progress of the celebration by a procession of tumbrils. They defied law, and denied the existence of everything with all the churlishness of ignorance. Corybantes of treason, they furnished the Republic with incapable generals and truculent journals. They placed high prices on the worst kind of demagogues and elevated obscure men who were attracted to the chase by the smell of blood. Everyone trembled before them. Hébert's coach held first rank. *Le Père Duchesne* was to be seen in theater boxes and in the restaurants of the Place of Equality. Paris shuddered, bending under the tyranny of these insults. The end, however, was near.

One day Robespierre who, under his mansard roof, observed everything, decided that it was time to put an end to this comedy. And he did.

How did he reach the conclusion that these fanatics and extremists in politics were invariably suspect? This truth, which has since been proved and which will doubtless find greater confirmation later on, was a mere assumption then, and Maximilien had to move with extreme prudence. It was not less surprising, when, tracking the traitors to their lair and finding nearly all of them in the Commune, he realized that, under all régimes and under all colors of opinion, the Hôtel de Ville of Paris necessarily sheltered a few rascals. It is in the nature of things; it is the ransom fate and the frivolity of Parisians demand. Robespierre having understood this, he soon found it quite natural that in so troubled an era the worst brothel should contain the worst men. Hardships do not debar knavery or treachery. Cut-throats can become the paid agents of foreigners. And these murdering braggarts, these bullying criminals, were they not royalist agitators? The limping scribbler Lepitre had conspired for the queen while posing as a Septembrist. In truth these officials of the city, so suspicious of patriots, were they so pure themselves? Robespierre who, nourished on Roman law, looked for the *cui prodest* in all political action, asked himself why on the 10th of August the municipal officials had so hurriedly appointed themselves as protectors of the Royal family. And why the Commune had failed to apply for legislative sanction in its proceedings against the prisoners of the Temple, which it had demanded in its proceedings against the King. Thus the Dauphin was the hostage of the Commune.

And the Incorruptible with his deep distrust asked himself further questions. In truth were these men incapable of turning a dishonest penny by seeking bribes from all the Courts of Europe, the emigré Princes, from Pitt, or the Convention? They had done worse.

So far as that went, Maximilien had taken his stand since the middle of 1793. Some time before he had made up his mind concerning these extremists of the Commune, who, as he said "would rather wear out a hundred red hats than practise a single virtue." Furthermore he knew that Hébert longed to cut his throat. Between them there was silent war, a war of intrigue and watchfulness. With every word and gesture Robespierre expressed his disgust at the affected rags of these false revolutionaries, who, placing themselves outside the Revolution, believed they cleverly escaped it. The eyes of the Incorruptible saw through them. They trembled before him. But soon reëmboldened they defied their patient enemy who, they believed, would never catch them redhanded.

It was at this time that Robespierre began to arm himself with police. He has been very bitterly assailed for this step, though, before seizing these rogues by the throat, it was necessary to find proof of their crimes. He took his time; this completely explains his pretended reconciliation with the Hébertists on the 25th of September, 1793, and the 9th Pluviose, 1794. So far as he was concerned their necks were already under the bloody triangle. But determined primarily to ruin their desolating power, Maximilien realized that neither eloquence nor virtue would be sufficient. He also knew that the connections the traitors had formed everywhere, from the Church to the Committee of Public Safety, would not be broken up without danger. To strike Ronsin was to threaten Collot d'Herbois, and to threaten Collot entailed Billaud. The silent and sacred power of the Committee might by being overthrown place the Revolution in peril. To wait, to watch, to seize the advantage, such was Robespierre's resolution, for he realized the audacity of the Hébertists would not try his patience for long.

Indeed the opportunity came precipitously. The 13th of March, after a grotesque attempt at insurrection, the Hébertist opposition fell like a rotten fence. Maximilien had only to step over it.

Hébert and his followers had openly prepared for a new massacre in the prisons. Robespierre was ill. For the first time they had screwed their courage to the point of attacking him, and made a call to arms.

At the first cry they saw not the insurgents appear, but Saint Just hastening from the frontiers. They felt they were lost and in fact they were. They wished to take advantage of the opportunity and to act while Robespierre was sick in bed. They hurried their preparations. To their misfortune Ronsin, who was always a braggart, met Souberville at the Tuileries and blabbed everything to him. Souberville, rushing off to Duplays, informed Robespierre, who heard the plan and turned pale.

"Revolutions have the most hideous aspects!" he cried. "Blood everywhere and always! Must the Republic devour itself! Ah! the scoundrels!"

This took place on the evening of the 24th Ventose.

CARTOON OF HÉBERT, LE PÈRE DUCHESNE,
RAGING IN PRISON.

Ten days later the Hébertists were carried away to their death and from my window I heard the mob, forever cowardly, shouting at them:

"He's in a buggerly rage, is the Père Duchesne!"

CHAPTER TWENTY-ONE

I SAW Danton a few times and I liked him. He was a vivacious man, turbulent, high-blooded, always in a hurry, and although as loquacious as the very devil, he continually seemed to be on the point of rushing off. You never saw him except standing, his hat in hand, accentuating his loud, strong voice with imperious gestures. He joked a great deal, thought little, and never wrote a word. He was negligent in his clothes, but without an affectation of Sans-Culottism, surrendering rather to that aversion toward stiff or elaborate dress which all large men seem to display. In such an exuberant and merry fellow, broad shoulders, muscles, a thick neck and a comfortable stomach were entirely in keeping.

Money melted in his hands. He spent whole fortunes on flowers alone. But, nevertheless, he went around the city wearing an ill-fitting coat of red ratine, a cravat tied loosely around his bare neck, his vest unbuttoned, his hair blowing in the wind, and huge top boots like a cart driver on his legs. From life he demanded pleasure and steaming clouds of praise. Prudery, like faith in posterity, seemed comical to him. Moreover, he made fun of everything.

Seated in the gardens of the Palais Royal he would tipple and deliver speeches to those around him.

"It's Danton!" passers-by would exclaim.

They listened and began by laughing. However, after a flood of obscene jokes, he would suddenly begin speaking from his heart and the crowd would be transported. Then, pouring himself out a bumper of wine from a dusty bottle, Danton would turn his back upon his enthusiasts and would amuse himself by making the whores and baggages who drank with him blush for very shame.

All affectation made him laugh but, with a prodigious gift of ridicule, he was without viciousness. This he well showed on the day when he said to Guadet:

"You are wrong. You don't know how to forgive."

Like all those who live in disorder, he had a happy air about him, the mild self-conceit of a triumphant rake. But in his anger there was never a man who was more arrogant.

The people loved him as he was. His huge body and impetuous temper emanated a kind of magnetism; he animated everything—friends, cafés, meetings, public squares, with a light-heartedness, a cordiality, a broad wit which very few people could resist. They would have followed him through hell. But those who were not immediately charmed, opposed him. Such a man left no one half-conquered.

Robespierre, it was quickly realized, was one of those whom Danton had not been able to enchant. How could a man like Maximilien, a meticulous politician, a man who lived like a clerk and who every evening signed each page of his note book, how could he love and understand this thundering whoremonger? Maximilien wrote ceaselessly, he wore out his eyes noting things down. Danton left behind only one thing in his handwriting, a love letter. Danton carried the destiny of the world in his head, mixed topsy-turvy with the addresses of light ladies and apostrophes upon kings.

Certainly Robespierre appreciated Danton as the vast cyclopean forger of the Republic, and certainly he did not disregard his past services to liberty, nor did he forget those many years they had struggled side by side; but the disorder and untidiness of the great orator, as well as his tender-heartedness and his enthusiasm, offended Robespierre's deep-rooted taste for temperance and severity. The Incorruptible, who was all reflection and thought, held the spontaneous genius of Danton in more than slight esteem.

Danton returned contempt for contempt, and gave good measure when he gave it. In his last days he smeared Robespierre's name with the dirtiest jokes. When someone whispered to him of danger, Danton pouring out wine and shrugging his broad shoulders replied:

"He dares not touch me: I am the Ark of the Covenant! Let him come near me! Robespierre! I will take him between my fingers and spin him round like a top!"

And he broke into his vast laugh, shaking his thick, ill-powdered hair. Such remarks were repeated to Maximilien, particularly by Vadier, who took upon himself the office of tale-bearer.

"You will laugh at this one," the honest hypocrite would begin.

But Robespierre, motionless, his face dark and attentive, would say nothing. What were his thoughts? Many a fisherman in troubled water would have liked to know. For many months the duel between the two leaders had been prearranged. Certain men went between them bearing malicious stories, yet Danton and Robespierre, doubtless realizing in what danger their antagonism might place the Revolution, curbed their desire for vengeance. Alas, they both died that their common enemies might triumph.

They were about the same age and their careers proceeded in similar channels. The fall of the old régime found them both struggling lawyers, equally poor and both burning with ambition. Then came 1789 with the Jabobins, the Cordeliers, the rivalries and agreements, the tribunes in which they were to follow each other in forced coöperation, the great sessions of the Convention, the struggles conducted on equal footing, all that one knows and all one cannot remember without dismay. For they died without knowing each other. Blind destiny! Their pride, so dissimilar, wrecked them. If Danton underestimated the power of his cold rival, Maximilien discovered only too late the game of those who, sacrificing Danton in Germinal, looked forward to glutting themselves upon him in the feast of Thermidor. Of what influence would the decrees of the Convention have had on the fatal night if Danton had filled the faubourgs with that thunder which, on August 10th, drowned out the clamoring tocsin? With

Danton present, there would have been no vengeful Thermidorians.

For what purpose would I drag up these past regrets? Without doubt it was the fulfillment of Vergniaud's prophecy that all the children of the Republic would murder their brothers.

At this point I come to the saddest part of my story. My pen trembles. Shall I speak out my doubts and my bitterness? I must. From those bright, eternal fields where these great men have become friends again, Maximilien calls me to be sincere, tells me his memory demands neither the charity of lies nor the hypocrisy of silence. I will tell everything. I will describe how the trial of Danton finally blasted our friendship which had been strained ever since the death of the Girondins.

CHAPTER TWENTY-TWO

SINCE Nivose I thought of warning Maximilien. More and more his followers kept him cribbed and confined. I scarcely ever met him in the rooms of the Committee. He seldom came there at this time, for having fallen sick he had been obliged to keep to his bed. Others more happy than I could undertake the task of drawing the two men together.

Meanwhile I watched them brewing Danton's death. Billaud-Varenne no longer concealed his fury; Nicolas the printer mysteriously produced proofs derived from the examinations of the Hébertists, and falsified by Coffinhal into accusations against Danton and his supporters; and old Vadier, casting all reserve aside, appeared before the Committee of General Safety to remark with a hideous grin:

"We will soon gut this bloated flounder."

It is said that during these days Danton was at Sèvres where the peasants saw him in his nightcap musing before his window.

One day Billaud-Varenne said in a loud voice in the anteroom of the Committee:

"Robespierre and Danton lunched together this noon at

Daubignay's house, along with Panis, Legendre, and Boursier."

Billaud laughed in saying this. He knew, or he believed he knew, that after a stormy conversation the two leaders had left the table almost reconciled. The next day, the 24th of March, at the Committee, Billaud said without any introduction:

"The time has come. Danton must die."

Maximilien rose from his chair, pale as death.

"They wish to kill off all patriots," he exclaimed.

I swear that he was profoundly sincere then. As little as he loved the dissolute and licentious Danton, the "Rotten Idol of Paris," he refused to cast him into the jaws of his enemies. In his estimation Billaud like Vadier were suspect. They advertised their zeal too widely. Moreover, Danton was the old Revolutionary of the past, and his name recalled so many dangers and hopes!

But the grave of the giant was already being dug in the cemetery of Errancis, even under the order of the Robespierrist, Payan. Everyone urged Maximilien to commit a blunder which he had no desire to commit. What is more, Danton, whether he abandoned himself to a false feeling of security, or whether he surrendered to a mortal weariness which, in certain hours, overwhelms men of action, moved no longer from his window.

Until the approach of the gendarmes, he believed that no man would dare raise a hand against him, not (as his friends have often slanderously asserted) that Robespierre had treacherously reassured him. Danton's confidence stemmed from his pride. I believe that if, on the 25th of March, Danton (warned at Sèvres by Fabricius Paris) had bestirred himself a little, Robespierre would have been able to save the Revolution from the bloody stain of Germinal. His first protest said as much. But Danton, hypnotized, fascinated by his fate, furthered the plans of his secret enemies, not only by his refusal to act, but by his furious attacks upon Maximilien whom he accepted, upon the word of scoundrels, as the prime author of the whole intrigue against him. These same scoundrels tempted Maximilien at the same time, until he finally lent an ear to their conspiracy.

Saint Just approved of it. The friendship, begun in the schools of the old kingdom, which united Maximilien to Camille Desmoulins, was sentimentality to this young man for whom everything dated from the Revolution. Moreover, there was the famous remark Camille Desmoulins had made; "Saint Just carries his head like a Holy Sacrament." To which Saint Just had savagely replied: "And I will make him carry his like a Saint Denis." His threat bore its fruit. In four days Robespierre reached the decision his disciple desired.

He abandoned Danton and Camille.

Was it a crime? No, if one considers the faults and vices of Danton; yes, if one believes that Maximilien lacked loyalty to such a point as to have secretly furnished Saint Just with notes for the latter's speech on the 10th Germinal, while on the night of the 9th he pretended that his consent to the arrest had been wrung from him.

It was a shameful capitulation, unworthy of his character. As everyone knows, his name appears the next to the last on the order for Danton's arrest, written on the back of an old envelope.

What follows is too well known to repeat: the absurd arrogance of Saint Just, apostrophizing the absent and fettered Danton from the height of the Tribune; the ignoble fright of Legendre; the melancholy and appalling speech of Robespierre; the joy of Vadier. That evening Maximilien said to Duplay:

"One must admit that Danton has chicken-hearted friends."

He spoke of Tallien, Thuriot, and Legendre, who were one day to take vengeance for these bitter words.

Robespierre was at the Committee when the news of the condemnation was brought him. It did not surprise him, since it was the second time the Revolutionary Tribunal had submitted to a decree of closure and thus subjected justice to a vote of expedience. The first decree which killed Vergniaud had been drawn up by Robespierre; the second, which killed Danton, was drawn up by Saint Just.

This took place on the night of the 15th Germinal. Before harvest time there was to be another meeting at night and another torch-lit assassination "for reasons of state policy."

CHAPTER TWENTY-THREE

WHEN all business was completed the Decembrists adjourned. It was about nine o'clock in the morning. I saw Robespierre leave, his face pale, the lids of his eyes livid, a great black cloak with a double hood flung across his shoulders. He walked alone, followed by Prieur and Carnot. Billaud remained at work, as did Saint Just. Barère followed Couthon's wheel chair.[1]

Maximilien, observing my presence, came over to where I was standing near the window. Our eyes met and he understood me.

Already his approaching glory had risen between us. I looked within him and I learned that in his proud, pure heart, an evil pride had entered. Had not the sacrifice of Danton been commanded solely by the safety of the country? Did not Danton die simply for having served d'Orléans and compromised himself with Dumouriez? But his death had opened the door to ambition. A barrier had been overthrown and it was for this, rather than for

[1] Both Couthon's legs were paralyzed. Carlyle, who never misses a chance to serve up any bits of scandal to discredit Robespierre and his followers, repeats the unfounded story that Couthon's paralysis was derived from having hidden in a peat-bog all night while an outraged husband hunted for him. *Tr.*

the condemnation of a traitor, that he felt happy. The death of the Moderates was the wage paid to the workers, who still believed—after twelve days—in the punishment of the Extremists. Dark plots, political machinations, rancor, ambition, unavowed designs; they all appeared to me in a flash, there, in these offices where haggard and exhausted men wandered like ghosts.

He was before me, motionless, his hat under his arm. My eyes met his sad, unyielding face. I straightened up, and shifting my eyes from his, I hurried away.

As I did so a porter came to tell Maximilien that his carriage waited at the landing. With the movement of a sleeper whom one suddenly awakens he turned and left. The door closed on his footsteps. In a shadowy corner under the hangings of tapestry, two men looked down into the garden. Passing near them I heard the rasping and cracked laughter of Vadier. He was saying to the hideous Vilate:

"Await death before praising a noble life."

* * * * *

BOOK THREE

CHAPTER ONE

A PECULIAR trait in my character makes me disinclined to resign myself to complete separation from a friend, even when I have desired the separation myself. I suffer from a vague feeling of regret. I try to overcome it, and, in fact, I can restrain myself sufficiently not to hazard vain or humiliating attempts at reconciliation. However, nothing I can do prevents a melancholy fancy from attracting me toward those places with which my memory is crowded.

It was for this reason I was so often seen during the early days of Prairial entering a restaurant which flanked the arch of the Duplay house. I supplied myself with feeble pretexts for going there. I made believe I lived in the immediate vicinity, although, as a matter of fact, the quarter did not lack more skilful and more widely patronized restaurateurs. But whatever attracted me there could not make me forget the mediocrity of the cooking. The commonplace and insignificant people who frequented the restaurant were house-stewards, sour bachelors, a few lawyers. But Nicolas the printer, the man with the club, appeared there—he who since the departure of Galandini for the front had assumed his position as Robespierre's bodyguard.

I learned from him that my name was often mentioned at the Duplays', but not without bitterness. No one ever mentioned the causes of our quarrel, and members of the salon could well have believed that our disagreement was entirely personal. The opinion of everyone—doubtless confirmed by Maximilien—was that in a fresh quarrel with his sister I had taken the part of Mlle. Robespierre. How touching was this reserve of his! A word from him would have cost me my position, and perhaps more.

During those days life was a dreadful thing. The Terror was increasing. Suspicion devoured our hearts. It was impossible to read the *Moniteur* without shuddering, for every morning the list of the condemned grew longer.

In Paris certain busybodies began to blame Maximilien for the severity of the law. The punishment of the factious groups, particularly of the Hébertists, gave credence to this belief, for the mob, unable to make distinctions, had become accustomed to think of the Incorruptible as the man who held the sword, the superintendent of the scaffold. This idea was skilfully fostered. Maneuvering with care, his enemies gained power by insinuating themselves into the good graces of those whose friends had been lost during October and Germinal. These movements against Maximilien started at the same point, that at which the two committees touched—or, in other words, at both sides of him and almost under his very eyes.

I longed to warn him, for I could see that the many mistakes and much brutality adroitly credited to him would eventually cost him his place in public esteem. If only I could have spoken in time! But, alas, everything kept us apart.

What happened to Robespierre is that which threatens all powerful men. His flatterers blinded him. His followers, more demonstrative than sincere, threw a vigilant guard about him, concealing the horizon and deceiving him about events. Misled as he was by his inherent distrust, as others are misled by too great a credulity, he chose his associates unwisely. The often critical voice of friendship was not heard in his chorus.

Twenty times I was tempted to go to the Duplays', but a stupid irresolution prompted by pride, embarrassment, jealousy, a thousand vague and confused feelings, restrained me.

Those who now haunted the house of the cabinetmaker, those whom I saw pass through the arch at twilight, were for the most part newcomers. The only one I knew was my sworn enemy, the squint-eyed Herman, my former schoolmate, like me the son of a court clerk of Artois. Before I had left Arras we had insulted each other, he as judge and I as advocate before the bar. Among the others were Dumas, who followed Herman as chairman of the Revolutionary Tribunal, Coffinhal, Payan, Fleuriot, and Topino the artist. Dr. Soubervielle, who never missed a meeting, loved me no more than he does now.[1]

All these people belonged to the Tribunal, in the capacity of judges as well as jury. Duplay, a juror himself, was swollen with pride. In his house one no longer breathed

[1] In 1825, Dr. Soubervielle lives in the quarter of St. Antoine, in Paris.

anything but the ill-smelling incense of a political sacristy. Thus did everything conspire to overthrow Robespierre, the great man who little by little was being imprisoned by his partisans.

It will perhaps be thought that I display too much passion, that I surrender to the resentment of an ousted friend. Nonsense! After so many years? Did I ever exhibit the slightest jealousy toward Saint Just and Lebas? Simon Duplay, the veteran of Valmy, whom I met occasionally on the street, thoroughly understood how I felt.

Brave little Simon, always the same! He dreamed of nothing but: Forward! With beating drums! With powder-flask filled! He regretted nothing, although if he had not lost his leg on the plateau of Valmy, he might have made a good general in the year IV, and then who knows . . .[1]

Our pleasure in meeting each other was always slightly overcast, for we had to meet furtively. Fundamentally he shared my opinion of Maximilien's entourage. Judging these matters as one of the common people, his good sense told him that the most diligent or assiduous men are not always the most trustworthy; and he suffered at seeing certain flatterers goad Robespierre in a thousand different ways to that distrust which was only too dominating a phase of his character.

Since the execution of Charlotte Corday, they had accustomed him to think of himself as surrounded by suspects and assassins. Duplay had equipped his doors with in-

[1] M. Simon Duplay is now deputy in the office of the Police Ministry.

numerable bolts and locks, and had even built a secret staircase. Little by little Maximilien's mediocre and fanatic friends brought about what everyone feared they would. His mind succumbed to the kind of languor common to overworked politicians, who can flourish only on constant adulation.

Robespierre, formerly so firm in his opinions, so scrupulous in his doubts, finally developed that fatal self-conceit of statesmen which blinds them to the distinction between disinterested praise and selfish flattery, and which inevitably leads them into accepting their confidents as their advisers. They refuse thereafter to listen to sincere advice, and even discredit obvious truths when they are disagreeable ones.

It is in vain that I question myself. I do not believe that at this time I could have put my friend on guard against those unseen but threatening perils which raised their heads around him. At my first words he would have imposed silence upon me. I remained mute. When chance brought us together in the rooms of the Committee, I turned away. One evening, the 12th of Prairial, he stopped near me, hesitating, without raising his eyes. I thought he was about to speak and I waited, feeling myself grow pale. But he raised his head and went off, looking unhappy.

Occasionally, when I remember these incidents, I imagine that Maximilien was beginning to understand my motives more clearly. I still can see him, his forehead dark with thought and anguish. Without the slightest doubt, he was struggling. Perhaps his fame terrified him; perhaps the thought returned to him, as it had during his sojourn in Arras, that great destinies are fulfilled in the proud solitude of unpopularity. But since then he was no longer his old self; the man had become the virtuous citizen, who thought himself impervious, like Mithridates, to the poison of vanity which popular adoration secretes.

Alas, the time came when everything urged him on toward a fatal triumph. Saint Just, who would have held him back, was far away. Upright Couthon saw nothing, neither the sly and cruel glances of Vadier nor Billaud-Varenne whetting his knife. O, that I had spoken on this evening of Prairial, sultry with unknown threats and mystery. To this vexed and weary leader I would have said that by cleaving to the symbols of power rather than to the nation he walked along the path of destruction. Perhaps I would have found, behind this leader of the "High-handed Party," that same man who three years before had said to the arrogant Dumouriez: "The people alone are great; the bauble of ministerial power vanishes when it is confronted by them."

Who knows? Perhaps I could have swerved him from this vain and majestic leadership, from the fatal apotheosis toward which fools and traitors led him. Was it possible that the sullen conferences of the Fouchés, the Ruamps, the Bourdons, the Lecointres, were not reported to him? Had he, too, reached that point of saying with a smile: "They dare not"—of dreaming with closed eyes, of anticipating the future under the caress of the warm air of June, of reaching forth toward popular favor with a hand which clutched only the air?

Alas, such was the state of his mind in those last days of Florial, when that ten day feast dedicated to the Eternal was being prepared, that civic Easter which was called the Feast of the Supreme Being, but which in reality was the deification of the Incorruptible. If on that day Paris, in the drunkenness of its own acclamations, did not see its idol totter, those who kept their eyes wide open were not deceived.

Yes, Robespierre learned and understood everything, during that fatal day. They thought him drunk with the incense of adulation. No. While the great citizen thoughtfully climbed the steps of the Capitol, he saw a chasm of emptiness and death at his feet.

The words of anguish he uttered at the Duplays' that evening have often been repeated:

"My friends, I will not be with you much longer."

Ah, even now, before the shadows of night have falien, this farewell to life already burned in his eyes. He knew himself called to judgment, and condemned. From the sepulchre, the mournful voices of his brothers rose to him, and, in the words of a friend, he understood that "for too long a time had be been called the Incorruptible."

CHAPTER TWO

I WAS at the *Champ de Mars* at the point in the Grenelle road just to the left of the arch through which the cortège passed on its way from the Tuileries.

A hundred drummers, preceded by mounted trumpeters, beat their drums with the sound of thunder. Then came the band, the cannon, and the pikemen. In the far distance, towering above the crowd, a chariot bearing a tree, a printing press and sheaves of wheat, lumbered on slowly.

Twenty-four Sections filed past in double column, the women on the left, bearing flowers, the men on the right, bearing oak branches. Then came soldiers under arms, and after them an empty space. And in this space a man walked alone, followed step by step by the clamor of multitudes. It was Maximilien.

For two hours he had advanced thus, as if borne along by the acclamations. A fabulous cry from a hundred thousand throats, rising from the very depths of Paris, entered by the triumphal gate and rolled on to the very foot of that symbolic mountain whither the Convention followed its leader.

It was the voice of a whole nation which swelled in

THE FEAST OF THE SUPREME BEING.

chorus, rose, thundered, breaking in waves against the embankments of buildings and houses, sweeping like a tide along the broad avenues, filling the air with its turbulent uproar, until it finally poured into the noble spaces of the *Champ de Mars,* with the thunder of liberated waters entering the sea.

And this voice cried:

"Vive la République! Vive Robespierre!

The cannon roared. The Convention, massed about the chariot and surrounded by tricolored ribbons, marched twenty feet behind the Incorruptible.

I see him now, and I shall always see him, as he appeared at that moment. He wore a blue coat which seemed to reflect the azure of a June sky, a white stock and vest, straw-colored breeches and striped silk stockings. Upon his ashen face there lingered a strange, stiff smile; his eyes were lowered, and in his trembling hand he clutched a bouquet of tricolored flowers. Dust covered his shoes. Though exhaustion plainly showed in both his body and his face, the crowd believed that he was merely drunk with wine.

That face, lined with the worry of sleepless nights, that heavy brow, those feet which felt their way unsteadily along the road, those weary arms which hung limp at his sides, filled me with immeasurable pity. Surrounded by this rapturous and shouting mob, I alone among them all realized the desolation of his heart which no fame would ever be able to assuage.

A man with bare arms, who stood by my side, exclaimed:

"Why aren't you cheering with us? Don't you admire Robespierre?"

I shouted with them. The man added, laughing:

"Good for you, my Royalist!"

How can I describe it? This spectacle, about which so much has been written—nothing like it will ever be seen again. An immense chorus sang Gossec's hymn, "Father of the Universe." More than five hundred thousand people covered the field. In the twilight, filled with the dust of summer, skyrockets burst brightly. Cannon thundered ceaselessly, and above their sound clamored all the bells of Paris. But alas, night came.

I was one of the first to leave. The city was almost deserted. A few barges drifted slowly down the Seine. While evening crept into the deserted streets, I wandered off, alone and weary, to sit on the terrace of the *Feuillants*. But soon a mob, swarming through the gardens of the Tuileries, announced the end of the Festival. I rose. As this mass advanced under the deep shadows, I saw that it crowded around the deputies, who, huddling together, still wore their feathers, which, caught by the occasional flash of a torch, gleamed in tricolored patches of light. As they approached me I could distinguish faces, and suddenly I gasped with surprise.

At Robespierre's heels the whole Convention in a tragic rout strode after him with their torn scarfs and faded flowers. Maximilien hastened on like one possessed who flees the babbling Furies. And indeed they were; it was a chorus of hate and envy which pursued him. Night had made them bold. Curses and imprecations burst from their unseen mouths, but Maximilien could recognize the voices of his enemies among them—of Bourdon, of Thirion, of mad Lecointre. And other indistinguishable cries rose as from a horrible abyss. At last the retinue reached the gate of the Château, and vanished.

Very late that evening I went to the restaurant in the Rue Saint Honoré. They were dancing under the street lights. Galandini, returned from the army, was pacing up and down before the cabinetmaker's, wearing the uniform of a lieutenant-general. A little later I saw Simon Duplay appear. He crossed over to speak to me.

"Well?" I said.

"Come."

He led me to the Duplay courtyard. Under the archway, he paused.

"Maximilien is lost," he said, in a low voice. "On the Bridge of the Revolution, today, disgust goaded him into a rebuke his enemies have been repeating everywhere: 'One would think Pigmies were attempting a conspiracy of Titans.' Those are his very words. Why couldn't he control himself? Now we must be prepared for anything."

"Then this explains the scene I witnessed at the Tuileries early this evening."

"Alas!"

We reached the center of the court. The house was dark except for Maximilien's room.

His slight shadow was silhouetted against the light, as

motionless as a pillar. We stared at it for a long time, the two of us, unseen and silent. Robespierre did not move.

The crowd was streaming toward the lights of the Tuileries, singing. Side by side, we walked slowly toward the deserted boulevards. When we were quite alone, the crippled soldier stopped, swore, wiped his forehead and muttered:

"The country is lost."

He gazed at me fixedly. I could find nothing to reply. Finally he took my hand, pressed it for some time in silence, then hobbled off. I saw him limp off into the night, toward the Seine, where the last fireworks burst against the sky.

CHAPTER THREE

In the morning of the 23rd of Prairial, about twenty citizens, packed together, heads up and ears cocked, were assembled on the terrace of the Tuileries. It was about eleven o'clock. A lifeless heat hung over the château and the gardens. From an open window which these twenty eavesdroppers were watching, issued the sound of angry voices. It was a window of the Committee room, where two of the Decembrists in a moment of fury forgot themselves to the extent of betraying the secret of the deliberations.

An attendant, catching sight of the listening group, ran to give warning. The window was closed, but too late. The eavesdroppers went through the city, spreading the news that there was a family row in the Committee. They had heard too much. A voice known to all—that high, clear voice which, the evening before, in public assemblage and in that very garden, had honored the Supreme Being—the voice of Maximilien Robespierre had cried:

"No one supports me; I am hemmed in by plots!"

The fierce voice of Billaud-Varenne answered:

"You would guillotine the whole Convention!"

Then, with the violence of desperation:

"I know you!" Robespierre shouted.

"And I know you, too, as a counter-revolutionist!"

At this moment the window was closed. Quite uselessly, for, at these words, which Billaud shouted at the top of his lungs, every member of the committee had stiffened into silence.

The Incorruptible had broken into tears.

At first everybody believed he wept from sheer rage, which would certainly have been justified by what had been happening in the committees during the last ten days. Insults were not a new thing there. Many times before had the Committee opposed the policy of Robespierre, and not without violence. He felt himself isolated in the midst of his colleagues. With all his powers, idolized by the whole nation, praised without stint by the journalists, master of the Jacobins and the Commune, controlling the police, appointing the Tribunal, subduing the Convention—with all this power Maximilien had lost his hold on the Committee. In fact, that very power of his caused it. For this committee of stormy patriots had become alarmed at an ascendancy which the cheers of the people during the festival had again sanctioned.

Due to the continual quarrels, as time went on, the relations between the members became increasingly bitter. They lay in wait for Maximilien. Formalists, like Carnot, were without pity; trimmers, like Barère, betrayed him; the fierce, like Billaud, bore an iniquitous hatred toward him. For, having isolated him, they now reproached him for standing alone. Even forgetting that Robespierre had fought against them to preserve Danton, they ended by blaming him for Danton's death. The accusation of dictatorship was brought up again and again. The somber but extravagant ardor of Billaud (always enflamed against the popularity of individuals) now turned upon the sole man whose popularity had raised him above the Revolution. And Billaud no longer concealed his hatred.

All of them, moreover, were ready to stake their lives in the struggle that was brewing, even though their suspicions were not in accord. Billaud feared a dictatorship of the Incorruptible. Barère believed Saint Just, rather than his chief, was being groomed for the rôle of tyrant. Carnot imagined a plot on the part of the Terrorists and had said to them: "As triumvirs you will perish!"

Finally the storm broke on that oppressive day of Prairial. The pretext for it was the famous law which, the evening before, Robespierre had caused Couthon to submit to the Assembly, without previously consulting the Committee.

This law of Prairial was a law of iron. Robespierre had modeled it, so to speak, on public calamities. Since it continued the Terror and accelerated convictions, it would, by the very excess of its rigor, revolt those inclined toward mercy. But no such mercy was to be found among members of the Committee. The anathema of the Decembrists was not at all justifiable. This law, placing the sword in their hands, made powerful judges of those who alone in the entire Republic opposed Robespierre. Less than any other could Billaud conscientiously defend his attack upon this decree. For was he not the first to propose a similar decree in November—that law of the 18th, which restricted to the Committee the right of ordering the arrest of representatives?

In addition, not one among his colleagues could be unaware of Robespierre's motives. All knew that under color of accelerating justice and making it more pitiless, he wished only to strike the survivors of Hébertism—those demagogues, those men of blood, the last emulators, avowed or concealed, of the Septembrists. Under the appearance of cruelty, the law of Prairial was intended by its formulator to put an immediate end to the Terror. It was not an unprepared scheme. It was a continuation of his policy, which, alone, had set itself the task of destroying the demagogues of the Commune, even back in those times when nobody took exception to any policy except Brissot's moderation. The "Immorals" of the year II, were in his eyes brothers to the "Wild Men" of '93.

Did they pretend astonishment that Robespierre should sharpen the guillotine on the morrow of that civic passover, when all believed the factions to be reconciled? But this haste was precisely an answer to the threats of his enemies. He was defending himself legally, before the Convention and by a vote of the Convention.

What, then, did Billaud's outburst mean? How was it to be explained? Very simply. The unpopular law offered to those who wished to destroy Robespierre, an unhoped for vantage. Far from annoying Billaud, it could not help but please him. No better occasion could have been offered. Never was anger better feigned. In the manner of Jupiter, Billaud insisted on the recall of a decree "which intimidated patriots." But he knew that, thanks to this decree, hereafter all the appearances of cruelty would be fastened on Robespierre, on the legislator of Prairial!

In reality, all these furious protests screened a deep and secret rejoicing. Collot d'Herbois did not rejoice less, he who thought of nothing but avenging Hébert. As to the members of the Committee of General Surety (almost all enemies of the triumvirate) they rubbed their hands in glee.

Robespierre, tired and irritated, did not see his error, and even committed a second more serious one by going before the Assembly to assume full responsibility.

On leaving this meeting, Lindet said to Vadier:

"We have the Incorruptible. He digs his own grave."

They had him, yes. At last. From this law of his they would squeeze every drop of horror they could. Unfortunate man! In vain could he protest that all this was done without him, that he had nothing to do with it, that he would resign from the Committee. The law was to be *his* law, enforced by *his* Tribunal. And when finally, worn out by this protracted carnage, everybody would cry: "Enough!"—when even the blood-thirsty rabble in the streets would stand speechless, when a besotted jury would pack off pell-mell to the guillotine conspirators, lunatics, assassins, drunkards, the starving and the innocent—then a hundred, no, a thousand men, from every corner of Paris would go about repeating:

"So this is what Robespierre desired!"

Such was the plan.

Vadier and others set themselves to the task. The frightful days of Mesidor began. They invented those conspiracies which seemed to turn the executioner into the guardian angel of the Incorruptible. They extended the route toward the guillotine and thereafter the tumbrils dragged their gasping burdens through the whole extent of the crowded quarters. From faubourg to faubourg, if necessary, the pavements of Paris would be smeared with blood. Revulsion would demand what pity had refused. On these stifling days of summer the cemeteries would be glutted with corpses. They would bathe the feet of the Idol in liquid putrefaction. The scaffold would be hardly more than an abattoir—until finally the public prosecutor, gone mad, would ask permission to rear the guillotine in court.

And all this—which is called Prairial and for which the gulled people blamed Robespierre—was organized by a master of crime named Fouché.

CÉCILE RENAULT SEIZED IN THE DUPLAY COURTYARD.

CHAPTER FOUR

One might say that Maximilien invited his own misfortune. From the 13th of Messidor he lost interest in everything. Even the affair of Cécile Renault could not arouse him from his lethargy.

She was a young girl, almost a child, who intended to assassinate the Incorruptible, à la Charlotte Corday. She was apprehended in the courtyard of Duplay's house, with two knives concealed in a market basket. Taken to the office of the Committee of Safety, where the indefatigable Vadier questioned her, she admitted everything they wished, and declared herself a Royalist. The evening before a certain man named Amiral had fired a pistol at Collot d'Herbois. Of these two affairs they made one tremendous case and called it the case of the "Red Shirts." It gave the enemies of Maximilien the occasion for which they had been looking.

First, the leaders of the Committee of General Safety caused the arrest of the father, mother and brothers of Cécile, then a few garrulous fools named Cardinal, Boïde, Pain d'Avoine, Porteboeuf, and the women Lemoine and Lamartinière. By a clever twist they included in the proceedings the case of two women, the Saint-Amaranthes, mother and daughter, spreading the report that the one was Robespierre's mistress and that the other had repulsed Saint Just. . . . They also threw in Comte Fleury, M. de Sartine, de Sombreuil, and four members of the police who were known to be Robespierre's enemies. In all, fifty-four persons, every one of whom was tried without delay.

It was then that Louis (du Bas-Rhin) induced the Committee of Public Safety to declare the condemned "parricides." They went to the scaffold dressed in scarlet, like Charlotte Corday, in six carts which for three hours had jolted through the streets of Paris. A hundred cannon were dragged along behind them. Similar pomp had not been seen since the execution of Louis XVI. And Voulland ran from one place to another, assuming a patriotic fury and shouting:

"This is the red mass! Down with the assassins of Robespierre!"

Others, bribed to do so, repeated this cry. Paris, horrified, turned against the Incorruptible. They began to call him the "Monster." And he, silent, aloof, let it be said.

He had resumed his long walks. With Broun close at his heels, he was seen in the gardens of Marboeuf, in the Montmorency Woods. To no purpose did his friends try to tear him from his melancholy dreams. "Brutus, thou sleepest!" they cried on all sides. Payan wrote him a letter, urging him to act. But in vain; Robespierre was weary. In his turn he was succumbing to that bitter, intense mortification, that surfeit which had enervated Vergniaud and Danton. Had he not, like them, over-estimated his powers? A fearful clairvoyance came to him. He lost faith in man, in reason, in the times. Even posterity seemed to him a stinking cesspool. He went toward his supreme battle with a worn-out heart.

CHAPTER FIVE

PARIS resisted; it hurt them to renounce the man who, only last month, was patriotism incarnate to a million Republicans. An attempt was made to ridicule him. After the tragedy, the farce. Catherine Théot, the visionary, announcing herself as the "Mother of God," had gathered around herself a group of proselytes as harmless as herself, who proclaimed Robespierre the Messiah. Seizing upon the actions of these mad people, Vadier poured a flood of ridicule upon Robespierre, accusing him of favoring their ceremonies and their delusions. Robespierre, in the chair of presiding officer of the Assembly and under the eyes of all, was forced to endure this derision without reply.

It whipped him into action.

But too late.

CHAPTER SIX

On the 5th of Thermidor I was in my office in the *Pavillon de Flore* when the noise of shouting rose from the garden. I leaned out the window. Robespierre had just stepped out of a carriage, on his way to the Committee.

He was hardly expected there. His colleagues, accustomed to his absence, did not dream of seeing him again until after the return of Saint Just. But Saint Just was secretly in Paris, back from the Sambre-et-Meuse with the news of victory.

Robespierre strode rapidly across the ante-chamber. . . . The ensuing conference was lengthy. They spoke in lowered voices, and the spies concealed behind doors, lurking behind the hangings, learned nothing for all their pains. If they divined that Maximilien's last attempt had failed, it was only by observing him depart, alone and downcast.

That very evening he left for Montmorency. As in all his hours of crisis, he went to ask counsel of the *manes* of Rousseau. Near this cottage to which he had come to pay homage as a young student trembling with hope and enthusiasm, now he came as an old man of thirty-six to meditate upon his farewell to posterity. It was here Maximilien drew up his last speech, the terms of his last will and testament, in these memory-haunted shadows.

Three days later, he mounted the rostrum before the Convention, and read:

"They call me tyrant. If I were, they would grovel at my feet, I would stuff them with gold, I would give them permission to commit all the crimes—and they would be grateful. . . . What am I—I, whom they accuse? A slave of liberty, a living martyr to the Republic, the victim as well as the enemy of crime. Every rascal abuses me. What would be considered unimportant and legitimate actions for others are considered crimes in me. If it were not for my conscience, I should be the most unhappy of men. Hardly a person has been arrested, hardly a citizen annoyed, who has not been told, 'There is the author of your suffering. You would be happy and free if he did not exist.' I will restrict myself to saying that for more than six weeks the kind and the degree of these calumnies and the powerlessness to do good and prevent evil have forced me to abandon my duties as a member of the Committee of Public Safety. I place my rôle as representative of the people above my membership in a committee, and I place my title as a man and a French citizen above all else. . . . Has France been the happier? I hope so. . . .

"In considering the multitude of vices the torrent of the Revolution has poured forth pell-mell with civic virtue, I admit that at times I have feared to be soiled in the eyes of posterity by the impure proximity of vicious men. Let them prepare the cup of hemlock for me; I will await it in this sacred hall. I have promised to leave a formidable testament to the oppressors of the people. I shall bequeath them the terror of truth and of death! No, Chaumette, no, Fouché, death is not an everlasting sleep. Citizens, efface from our tombstones that blasphemous maxim, which casts a mourning veil over nature and which is an insult to death. Engrave there, rather: 'Death is the beginning of immortality!' "

The Convention listened in silence, touched in spite of itself by this pathetic voice. But it was an assembly and it suffered from the weakness of assemblies, which demanded that names be mentioned. While speaking, Robespierre had looked fixedly at those he wished to indicate: Tallien, Fouché, Bourdon, Lecointre, Fréron, Dubois-Crancé, Ruamps, Bentabole—in short, all those toward whom the law of Prairial was directed, the law they had used against Robespierre, without his support, in guillotining twelve hundred prisoners during the single session of Messidor. . . .

The Convention, though it admired this noble and mournful speech, expected something more. They would have preferred accusations and names. By veiling his attacks, the orator defeated himself. All believed themselves threatened. Those who (quite certainly) would have surrendered his enemies to him, had he named them, were transformed at one stroke into a trembling and snarling pack.

Such a grave error in tactics can be explained only by

Maximilien's prolonged absence. Solitude is not a good councillor of statesmen. He had returned to the world of anxious and impassioned existence with words addressed to the future. Previous to these ten days of idle meditation, it cannot be doubted that Robespierre would have conducted the attack differently. Knowing that fear alone controls senates, he would have unhesitatingly named his enemies. They even expected it. Most of them could no longer sleep quietly in their beds. For a month Bourdon had been sweating with terror.

When it was over and he had left the platform, all breathed deeply. By sacrificing action to rhetoric, Maximilien had fired on them with wet powder. Now these men, reassured and jubilant, saw their former fears sweep through the whole Convention. Panic had saved them.

A vote was taken on the question of printing the speech, which at first was decided upon, but was finally abandoned. By his signal error, Maximilien had brought about the union of his enemies, those in the Convention and those in the Committees. The brutal voice of Billaud was now heard. Barère put in his word. Robespierre read the signs, and saw that he was vanquished.

"I have thrown away my shield," he said. "I have left myself open to my enemies."

He went back to Duplays'. That evening he was to read his speech to the Jacobins. In the interval, to relax, he went for a stroll in the Champs-Elysées. Eléonore went with him. It was a warm, luminous evening. The sun purpled the horizon toward Chaillot, with a deluge of blood and flame. Eléonore, pressing close to her fiancé, said:

"It will be fine weather tomorrow."

Maximilien made no response.

At the club he was welcomed with delirious enthusiasm. When he had finished the reading amid tears and rapture, he bowed his head and tossing his papers on the table before him, said in a weary voice:

"Brothers, this is my last testament. Today I have faced the confederacy of rogues. I succumb without regrets. You will see me drink the hemlock calmly. I leave you my memory. Defend it!"

At these words, all the Jacobins, raising their arms, took the oath after the manner of the Romans. Then, in the shadows, they discovered Legendre, Collot and Bourdon, come there as enemies to spy upon Maximilien. Ordered out of the hall, they skulked away. Collot alone lingered to attempt an explanation. They drove him out ignominiously.

At this moment Payan approached Robespierre and whispered:

"The people will follow you. Let us overthrow the Committees."

Maximilien shook his head in refusal. He intended to start the decisive battle the next day, at the Convention. Payan realized that victory lay in the street—that the hour for oratorical struggles was past. But restrained by his respect for the Incorruptible, he said nothing more and rejoined Coffinhal who awaited him in the courtyard.

"Well?" asked the latter, brusquely.

Payan shrugged his shoulders.

"You see? His integrity won't let him consent to an insurrection. *Ah foutre!* Since he won't have us save him, let us go to his defense and prepare to avenge him!"

Meanwhile Maximilien returned home. Madame Duplay saw that his face showed signs of distress; under his eyes were rings of fatigue. He would say nothing but:

"I no longer expect anything of the Mountain. But the majority are pure."

Having spoken, he returned to his room, again to weigh his rhetorical periods on invisible scales. His last night was passed in work. He wrote, then rose and paced back and forth in his room. Outside he could occasionally hear raised voices, or from time to time the hoof beats of a horse. Then he would go back to his work and cover page after page with writing. Finally with folded arms he awaited the morning, in the fitful light of the candles.

Well before the session of the Jacobins had adjourned, Saint Just had taken himself to the Committee. He entered slowly, greeted the others with a cold nod, and without noticing the look of interrogation upon their faces, began to write.

At midnight Collot dropped in, driven from the Jacobins, still suffering from bruises and fuming with anger. Saint Just, sarcastic and cold, asked him:

"What has been going on at the Jacobins?"

"You! You dare to ask!"

They threw themselves at each other, and had to be separated. Such was the impassivity of Saint Just that, having straightened his clothes and tied his cravat, he resumed his writing. Barère, seeing that he ran little risk, stepped up and said:

"You're scoundrels. You wish to divide the spoils of the country among a cripple, a child, and a monster. I wouldn't give you a back yard to govern. . . ."

Saint Just shrugged his shoulders. Then Collot said:

"I'm sure he has his pockets full of libels."

Saint Just, without a word, emptied his pockets on the table and returned to his writing.

This went on until day came, with alternate moments of calm and violence. Saint Just, inscrutable, continued his work, occasionally responding to abuse without ceasing to write.

Just as the dawn of the 9th Thermidor brightened the sky, he folded up his speech, put it in his pocket, took up his large hat, straightened his vest.

He went off with a deliberate step, leaving the large door open.

The others, gloomy and furious, began their deliberations. Carnot alone was unmoved. Toward ten o'clock they were still there, awaiting the return of Saint Just, who was to read them his report. They saw Couthon arriving, in his wheel-chair. Carnot was speaking of arresting Henriot and the mayor of Paris. They had begun their arguments again when a messenger appeared from the Convention, who announced:

"Saint Just has taken the floor."

They left at a run. In a moment the pavilion was abandoned. Couthon's wheel-chair rolled through the empty corridors.

****

CHAPTER SEVEN

THE weather was hot and sultry. Above Paris the low sky seemed to presage a storm. A few fishermen were casting their lines in the Seine. Toward eleven o'clock the air became intolerably oppressive.

Meanwhile crowds were gathering in the lower balconies of the Convention. There had been a line waiting since dawn, laughing and joking as usual. I explained who I was to the gendarme stationed in the vestibule of the small chamber. Thus did I have the sad pleasure of being present at the session, in a draped loge behind the president's chair. Several municipal officials, members of the police, and known functionaries also entered. We took our seats.

As the crowd swarmed over the platform and the amphitheater, there was a loud clatter of sabots on the wooden steps. By noon not a single seat remained. It was stifling. Under the great arched roof, on the tiers of benches where the people had gathered, was a vast, varicolored surge of noisy humanity, a crowd of soldiers, workers wearing carmagnoles, and the knitting women. Below, on the side platforms, were the henchmen of the Committees, some of them armed with clubs or even with sword canes. There were others, with the faces of spies. And finally the worried bourgeois, who seemed to be on the alert for heaven knows what. In all, fifteen hundred persons, and an unforgettable odor.

The deputies entered. The benches were quickly filled. The faces of these men, seated side by side, revealed their emotions like open books. Some were pale, nervous, trembling, in fear of their lives. The faces of others, less terror-stricken, were filled with the hope of bloody vengeance. Among them were those who were gray and wearied, who came there after a sleepless night. And others were present, the veterans of the Constituent Assembly, who surrounded Sieyès and who, voting complaisantly, had avoided death by renouncing their principles, and had thus passed unscathed through the whole Revolution. Bowing and scraping between the posts of the guillotine, they had squirmed out from under the knife. Shouts and a ruffle of movement announced each entrance. They impatiently awaited Tallien, who lingered in the antechamber for his cue. Maximilien came in with the last arrivals.

Suddenly I heard, near me, the stroke of a bell—two, three; the vibrations spread through the uproar, then everything was silent. Saint Just had arisen. Clenching a roll of manuscript, he ascended the steps to the tribune. He unrolled his papers, held them in both hands before him, and turned his whole body, elbows close to his sides, toward that part of the Assembly he wished to address. His voice rose, cold, flat, unemotional. He said:

"I belong to no faction; I fight them all. They will be

checked only by institutions which will offer guarantees, which will place a limit to authority and which will keep human pride bent under the yoke of public liberty."

While he was speaking late arrivals were taking their seats noiselessly. Maximilien followed their movements; he seemed to appraise them at a glance; then he turned his eyes toward the upper door of the chamber, where the crippled veterans sat, as if he were expecting the arrival of someone who was late in appearing. After a moment he took off his glasses and replaced them with others, a round, shell-rimmed pair which he used in reading.

I could not take my eyes from him. He was calm but very pale. His sky-blue coat—the one he had worn at the Festival of the Supreme Being, and had not put on since—was a bright spot of color in the midst of the Assembly. With his carefully powdered hair, a stylish and immaculate stock, he never had appeared more of a dandy. He had gone to a brawl as if dressed for a wedding.

Above, Saint Just was reading.

"The stream of events has proved that this rostrum is perhaps the Tarpeian Rock for him who would come . . ."

At these words Tallien burst into the room. He had waited for this moment. Everything was ready, hounds and hunters. They began to fling the quarry to the dogs. . . .

On his entrance Tallien shouted in the loud voice of an actor:

"I demand the floor for a motion of order!"

Against all rules of parliamentary procedure the president gives him the floor. Saint Just protests, but in vain. Tallien raises his voice:

"I demand that the veil be torn away!"

Billaud runs up, his forehead white, his eyes flaming. He snarls forth his speech. One would say that his fury of the 23rd of Prairial possesses him again. He no longer can control himself. Before the Assembly, he vomits pell-mell his accusations against the Jacobins and the secret quarrels between Committee members. The public tries to understand.

I see Robespierre rise and run to the tribune. But already Tallien has ascended from the other side. The three stand jostling each other on the platform. Billaud continues. His voice is harsh, choked by his own violence. In spite of the encouragement of his party, his fury throttles him into silence. . . . Tallien relieves him; nothing can tire Tallien. Robespierre tries to elbow his way between them. They thrust him back. Tallien raises a poniard, and Robespierre offers his breast. He tries to speak. But no! At every attempt the bell rings and a hundred voices in full cry howl him down. He cannot speak. They will not let him. He is to die silent, gasping for breath, baited like a beast. Little by little his voice breaks. . . .

Since the play must be kept going, a new actor is thrust onto the stage. It is Barère. There are four, now, on the platform. Maximilien, repulsed, jostled, clings to the tribune with all his might. Ignominious spectacle!

O faithful memory, sustain me! Letting my pen fall

from my hands, I live again those hours; again I see that dust, that haze pierced with yells and insane gestures. Maximilien is there, pale in his blue coat, hat in hand, shaking his fist at the threatening mob. I see him, hemmed in, running along the tiers of benches, entreating for death, while the Mountain wait, their arms crossed, until he shall strangle with anger, with misery, and with fatigue.

"Down with the tyrant! Down with the tyrant!"

He descended. At the rear of the hall was the obscure dead-water of the Marsh [1] and here he seemed to lose his footing.

"To you, good and virtuous citizens," he cried, "to you I will speak and not to those brigands. . . ."

All were silent, turning away their eyes.

All this returns to me—his wan face, dripping with sweat, which he constantly wipes away; the laughter; the jests tossed from bench to bench; the commotion of the public; the thousand dark faces at the edge of the galleries hurling sarcasms into the pit, like stones.

The dénouement was near. Robespierre was hoarse. Maddened, he kept no strength in reserve, exhausting his last powers in useless protests. His enemies saw him sinking.

Then they wished to completely degrade him, so Vadier was summoned. The old clown babbled nonsense about the Mother of God. Laughter was showered on Maximilien like the blows of cowards who strike only the

[1] The Marsh or Plain represented the party of the Center in the Assembly. *Tr.*

defeated. Nevertheless, laughter is allied to pity, and Tallien, who feared the slightest risk, interrupted Vadier:

"Bring the discussion back to its real point!"

Robespierre leaped to his feet. "I can bring it to the point!"

"Down with the tyrant!"

Again the bell. No, he was not to be granted a word. Only the great voice of Danton could have made itself heard. Ah! At this hour with what bitterness Maximilien must have remembered that dinner at the *Marais,* that last interview when the athlete had given him his hand. . . . With one blast of his lungs Danton would have driven off these dogs! How his roaring would have routed the pack!

Maximilien wiped his forehead. Pale, stubborn, he had ended by taking refuge at the foot of the tribune, and there he persisted in his demands that he be heard. His every appeal renewed the shouts of the mob.

"Down with the tyrant!"

The dust seemed to thicken; the odors became more acrid. Above the tumult, Thuriot's bell clamored as if on the quarter-deck of a sinking ship.

Nobody saw, nobody heard anything more. The only image which remained fixed in the memory of witnesses is of Robespierre in desperation, struggling to the bitter end.

"For the last time, president of assassins!"

He was unable to finish. Then a voice was heard:

"The blood of Danton chokes thee!"

At these words Maximilien found strength to collect himself.

"So it's he!" he cried bitterly. "It's Danton you think you avenge, cowards!"

He began to laugh. With this, he waived aside all that murderous hooting, which no longer troubled him. Without flinching, he saw Fréron rise to cry:

"Ah! How hard it is to pull down a tyrant!"

Meanwhile, Tallien began again to stir up the conspirators. He explained that Maximilien had deserted the Committees only that he might oppress without further hindrance. Then Robespierre, a last time, threw himself forward:

"That is false, I . . ."

More hooting. Then the whole Convention, standing, raised their arms to pass by acclamation an order for Robespierre's arrest, just submitted to them by Thuriot.

It was then that Maximilien recovered his calm. He went over to his brother and sat down. An usher approached to hand him the decree of accusation. After reading it, he stuck it in his hat.

"To court with them!" the mob howled.

They rose and departed, first Maximilien, followed by the haughty Saint Just. Couthon was carried out.

The crowd applauded frantically.

"There go the high-handed party!"

But Lebas had arisen.

"I will not share in the disgrace of this decree," he cried.

They tried in vain to hold him, but he left his coat in their hands and joined the vanquished chief. The younger Robespierre stood up.

"I will share the fate of my brother!"

The Assembly had done its work. Beside me, in the loge, a little bespectacled man pulled out his watch and said, with a satisfied air:

"It's twenty to four."

I rushed out of the small room and ran toward the Hall of Liberty. A shouting mob was there. All those who had been unable to find room in the galleries were standing in two rows, waiting to see the defeated members leave.

The door, hung with green draperies, swung open.

The five appeared, surrounded by gendarmes. Couthon, smiling, clung to the shoulders of two guards, who carried him seated on their crossed hands. Saint Just, his head bare, followed. But the crowd, made up for the most part of bare-armed *Sans-Culottes,* national guardsmen, market-women and Section orators, had no eyes or voice except for Maximilien. They did not yet dare, however, to go too far in their insults, for his cool, steady glance, his self-assurance as he passed them, impressed them with his power.

Meanwhile the crowd formed a hooting procession behind the prisoners. Thus they descended the grand staircase. A peddler of books, newspapers, pamphlets and lists of suspects [1] who owed his concession to Maximilien, proved himself to be no ingrate. Pulling off his cap, he

[1] After the passage of a law in September, 1793, not only Moderates were "suspect" and subject to immediate arrest but also those who "having done nothing against Liberty, did nothing for it." All prisoners arrested on this charge were obliged to support themselves at their own expense. *Tr.*

CHAPTER EIGHT

I REMAINED there, my face pressed against the win…
An order came to lead out…
shouts of the soldiers, the…

to the Committee of General Surety. Without doubt they were led there to dine and for examination. They were kept there for over an hour.

Without much difficulty I managed to reach the entrance to the offices. There I waited, reading Tallien's journal, the *Spectateur Français*, which a clerk had lent me, still damp from the press.

I expressed my disgust in a loud voice. But no one thought of troubling me; none of all the informers with which the place was infested took notice of my words. There was a vague uneasiness in the air, increased by the members of the two Committees passing from one door to another.

It was here, amid this disorder and noise, that the chain of events and circumstances began which determined Maximilien's conduct, and gave it the name of "the Enigma of Thermidor."

It was no enigma whatsoever. The succession of events made Robespierre their plaything only in so far as they surprised him. In the first place, he did not believe in an insurrection. Not only did it seem impossible to him, but he did not see the necessity for it. A parliamentarian, he had placed his first hope in legal measures. But the uprising forced his hand. Then he acted otherwise than is generally believed. As for his motives, he did well in carrying them to the tomb with him.

With remarkable clairvoyance—which did not remove his suffering and agonies—he foresaw the misconceptions posterity would cherish of him. His conduct, in its more human aspects (that is to say, the most noble of sentiments mixed sometimes with instinctive revolts and sometimes with the excesses of a harassed mind) this conduct, I say, would have been accepted in Vergniaud; it would have been understood in Danton. But it did not accord with Robespierre's character. He understood this perfectly, and he kept silence. Since then they have searched everywhere for a truth which a knowledge of human beings shows large and clear: the defeated man of the 9th of Thermidor, long accustomed to control events, suddenly found himself swept along in their course. He was like a swimmer betrayed by the tide. He struggled, he fought back, then he was caught up in the flotsam. He attempted the impossible, then gazed at the sky despairingly before he sank.

But I must return to my story where I left it off. God give me strength!

CHAPTER NINE

PACING back and forth, I waited before the Committee of Surety. At the end of about an hour I saw Amar arrive. He crossed the antechamber rapidly. As the door swung open for a brief moment, a confusion of voices burst forth, dominated by the shrill falsetto of Maximilien. What was happening in there?

I stepped to the window. A wind had arisen, a low, sultry wind which raised little spirals of dust in the garden. The sky was dark and lowering, but still rain did not fall.

A Committee bailiff was summoned. They had just reached a decision—to take the accused to the secretariat, to serve them dinner. At this moment a great tumult arose in the antechamber and Henriot appeared, with his aides-de-camp.

He was not drunk, as has been maliciously reported. He was vehement and rough, as was his nature on occasions requiring violence. When they refused him entrance, he kicked open the door. His intention, which he proclaimed in a voice that shook the building, was to deliver the prisoners on the spot. But the gendarmes of the tribunals, commanded by the brigadier Joanolle, threw themselves on him. They bound him, and locked him up.

A little before seven o'clock, Robespierre and his party, who had just finished their meal, were informed that they were now to be taken to their prisons. Maximilien asked for a cup of coffee, which was sent for. Then five groups of gendarmes and guards advanced.

Here begins the imbroglio.

CHAPTER TEN

WHILE the Robespierrists were dining and deciding unanimously to submit to the decree of arrest in order to acquit themselves before the Revolutionary Tribunal, the five wardens of the five prisons had received a message:

"Citizen warden, we command you, on your responsibility, to exercise every precaution that no letters or papers enter or leave the place of detention under your charge, until you receive further orders.

"You are furthermore forbidden to receive any prisoners, or to place any one at liberty, except by express command of the police administration."

This order came from the Hôtel de Ville. In the two hours which had just passed since the vote of the Assembly and the end of the session, the Commune—advised the night before by Coffinhal and Payan—had decided against the Convention in favor of the accused. Henriot's violent attempt to rescue was the first act of the insurgents; the second was the order to the prison guardians; the third was the immediate convocation of the Commune at the Hôtel de Ville.

Then, along with this command to keep their prison doors shut (which they would probably not have obeyed) the wardens received another, a secret order, this time from the Committee. This order was executed by every one of them; meanwhile they asked themselves, like Beaumarchais' Basile, which of the two parties was the dupe, since both commanded the same thing: *not to execute the law.*

But why should the Committee of Public Safety give secret orders to disobey those which it issued in full daylight? No one will ever know.

Maximilien, surrounded by his gendarmes and his guard, was crossing the Seine. About seven o'clock I arrived at the Luxembourg, close behind him. A mob had escorted us through the streets. Everywhere we met the mounted guards of the Commune, bearing orders for an insurrection.

At the Rue de Tournon the gendarmes had to force their way through the crowd. A mob of armed patriots had surrounded the prisoner, howling:

"More power to the Commune!"

And so it went until we neared the prison. Far off, in the light of the declining day, was something that seemed to be a thicket of bayonets, swaying in the wind.

Before the prison gate we found a municipal officer, covered with plumes and insignias, who roundly berated the gendarmes and the guard.

"Must I hold you up to the scorn of all good citizens?" he shouted. "You who have dared to lay your hand on the friend of the people!"

The crowd cried:

"Long live Robespierre!"

The gendarmes, resolute enough until now, did not know what to do. It was the prisoner himself who settled the matter.

"Take me," he commanded, "to the office of the municipal police."

They yielded. The march was resumed to the sound of the tocsin. Everywhere drums were beating. Arriving at the Quai des Orfèvres, we met a large party of artillery men who were dragging their batteries toward the *Hôtel de Ville*. They came to a halt and, wiping their foreheads with their caps, cheered the prisoners. The Convention seemed to be defeated.

Of what was Maximilien thinking? Why did he not now take his way to Faubourg Saint Honoré? Why did he not have himself led in triumph to his humble room in the Duplay house?

"Nobody," I said to myself, "would dare drag him from this sanctuary. A section of pikemen, constantly on the look-out, would have guarded him there day and night. All Paris would have taken Robespierre under its protection."

A strange project? Perhaps. In any case, I was alone in entertaining it. The current was sweeping Maximilien toward the Place de Grève and the Hôtel de Ville. He resisted. He ended by persuading them all to take him where he wished to go. Soon the procession arrived at Police Headquarters. The gendarmes, having no orders and, in addition, fearing that this excited mob would turn against them, retired.

At this moment I decided to slip in beside Maximilien. He was seated in the midst of the police officers. Sullen men surrounded them, alert, ready to swing their sabers or to fire on anyone who dared profane their idol.

I approached. Robespierre saw me and gave me his hand.

It was burning. I held it a moment. On the hard faces around us I observed something akin to tenderness. Maximilien was about to speak when the door opened and a delegation of six entered, coming from the Commune. One Michel Lasnier was its leader. They had been joined by Coffinhal and ten Section members, who had just delivered Henriot from prison, right under the nose of the Convention. The General was storming; he shook himself as if he still could feel the cords which had bound him. He raged like a dragon in the middle of the room, amid the general uproar.

Meanwhile Michel Lasnier succeeded in making himself heard.

"Robespierre," he said, "I come to you on the part of the Commune. We wish to remind you that you do not belong to yourself; you belong entirely to France. Your brother is at the Hôtel de Ville, where he sits among the patriots of the Executive Committee."

Instead of replying, Maximilien questioned him. He wished to know how Henriot had been delivered, and by whom. Coffinhal and his party had struck like lightning on the headquarters of the Committee of Surety. There was no resistance. All the Convention guards had themselves joined the brave *Sans-Culottes* of the Commune—all, even the gendarmes!

"Then," I said, "are you going to stop there?"

Everybody present looked at me. Many divined my thought, and agreed with me. None suspected that the hour for an easy victory had now passed, and that from now on another occasion would not arise. None, I say, except perhaps Maximilien. I read his eyes. And I understood, in an instant, that the insurrection came to him as a complete surprise, that he opposed it, not because of his respect for legality (as some have since believed) but because of the plan which he and his friends had agreed upon, during dinner. Loyal to this plan, which was to obey the law and to face the music before the Revolutionary Tribunal, he refused to leave.

Coffinhal insisted.

"What are you waiting for?" he said. "The armed populace is gathering. On with our opposition! Let us at them! Come!"

Maximilien, head in his hands, remained motionless. I could hear him say very low, almost in a whisper, as if he were questioning himself:

"Are not the opposition those who refuse obedience to the sovereign will of the people?"

"What's the matter?" was the impatient cry raised from all sides. "What are we waiting for?"

"To arms!"

"Hurrah for the pikemen!"

I saw him straighten his shoulders. Our eyes once more

met. He smiled at me sadly. Outside we could hear the drum beating the call to arms.

"Come," said Henriot.

"No," answered Maximilien.

Then Lasnier left. Coffinhal was like a goaded bull; Henriot upon leaving spewed forth a torrent of oaths. For almost an hour we remained in the greatest disorder. Every extravagance men can think of on occasions like this was uttered. Toward half past ten a cavalryman arrived alone, bearing a short note:

"The executive Committee, appointed by the Council, needs your advice. Come immediately."

Robespierre arose.

The bells of the Hôtel de Ville pealed ceaselessly. A populace drunk with noise, heat and wine clamored under the windows, while rolling drums neared or grew distant.

"To arms!"

Robespierre was seized upon and dragged to the windows.

"You will ruin me," he murmured.

But the crowd had recognized the coat, the powdered hair. Cheers broke out. There were eddies and swirls in the mob gathered below; the tocsin sounded constantly; there was a clanking of pikes and sabres, a clattering of sabots—a tremendous clamor, furious, continuous, deafening.

"Long live the Commune! Long live the Commune!"

"Long live the Republic!" replied Robespierre.

They shoved him toward the entrance. He made the

resigned gesture of a man who accepts his fate; then, quickly crossing the room, his followers behind him, he disappeared under the arch where shadows in uniforms held smoking torches.

CHAPTER ELEVEN

HE went on, amidst shouting and singing. Death was in his heart. At certain times during their progress he faltered so visibly that his neighbors, believing him overcome with fatigue, dared to support him by putting a hand under his arm, in spite of his well-known dislike for such familiarities.

In reality, Maximilien had an insight into the situation which none of the rest of us had. For everyone overestimated the actual power of the Commune over the Sections. A large number of Sections most active in their loyalty to the Commune of 1793 opposed the Commune of 1794.

Robespierre was to pay for the death of the Hébertists and he knew it. He knew that *his* Commune, the new one, was only a strong and sure power while he, Robespierre, was known to be in accord with the Committees. It no longer was that powerful authority of workers, supported by the glory of the 10th of August and the impunity of September. Robespierre himself had weakened it—had indeed, desired it to be weak. The men belonged to him; but how few among them had the souls of leaders! Certain Sections, moreover, would not obey him, would have been only too glad to hold him at their mercy, and, if possible, to make him expiate the deaths of Jacques Roux and of Marino. In many a vicious and sordid lair the municipal officers were thought to be his creatures. They would not have dared show themselves in such places, in broad day, with their plumed hats, their sashes, their gold-buttoned vests, their gray coats, without being scoffed at and stripped naked. At night time it would have been a massacre. The thirtieth Section belonged to Tallien; Arcis, its neighbor, would follow it. What is more, the *Cité,* which controlled the great bell of Notre Dame, was opposed to an insurrection led by the Commune. Even La Grève might declare itself against the Hôtel de Ville.

Robespierre knew all this. However, he marched on. He followed his destiny, in the midst of a hundred fools, so completely deafened by themselves they could not observe that the echo of their enthusiasm was lost in silence. And these hot-heads laughed and sang without seeing the terrible face of Paris, the night executioner of insurgents when she denies them her calloused hands, her blood and her barricades.

In this a single resource remained to Maximilien, one hope still inspired him—to find at the Hôtel de Ville Saint Just, Robespierre the Younger, Lebas, to summon Couthon without delay, to persuade all of them, cost what it might, to return to their prisons, if necessary to have the prison doors forced open by the people, and there—surrounded by what a halo!—await their trial before the revolutionary jury.

Maximilien grasped at everything. How could he suspect that Saint Just, the very child of his mind, his dearest disciple, was to oppose his chief's wishes and was to give him with his own hand the call to arms. . . . But let us not anticipate.

Toward nine o'clock we reached the Hôtel de Ville. The arrival of Robespierre was announced. Hardly had we appeared when the Council ordered the chandeliers illuminated as on special celebrations.

Our troop submerged the five hundred municipal guards, in their sashes. Lights flared; Maximilien advanced amidst cheers which made the old building tremble. Lebas, Saint Just and Augustin were standing there, waiting for Robespierre. Exaltation was on all faces.

Especially Robespierre the Younger, who at Toulon had formed a taste for rash enterprises, was all impetuosity. He talked of breaking down the doors of the Convention with cannon shot. Saint Just added phlegmatically that since the Assembly had excluded the five from the discussion without a hearing, it had itself renounced its inviolability.

"The people," said he, "will know what use to make of this *coup d'Etat* and by defending its oppressed representatives will once more save the Fatherland and Liberty."

Payan, who could no longer contain himself for excitement, sent for the book of the Rights of Man, and Coffinhal in his great voice read the 35th and last article of the Constitution of 1793, which sanctions the right of revolting against the government when the rights of the people are endangered.

Frenzied applause followed this reading; the people massed outside, though they could hear nothing, nevertheless applauded.

How was this to be resisted? Something outside Maximilien had controlled the maneuver, had decided the battle.

It was almost midnight. The Convention was in session. One word from Robespierre would still have sufficed. The Sections hostile to the triumvirate had as yet taken no action; the loyal followers were ready to strike. So much indecision could be turned to profit and even with inferior numbers, the representatives could be surprised and seized during the night. With the dawn, Paris would side with the conqueror. . . .

But Maximilien shut his ears. He was waiting.

For what?

Nothing.

Perhaps deep in his heart he hoped that the uprising, from now on inevitable, would break forth without his order, as if in spite of him. Thus he could play two cards. Every statesman when pressed by circumstances plays this game.

At twelve-thirty he was still talking against time, yet without opposing the enthusiasm of his supporters.

"No," he said, "we must not yield to the importunities of a handful of the opposition. It is their business to take the Convention by surprise. Those traitorous deputies, their accomplices and their satellites would then have to answer for their conspiracy against liberty, which they formed to crush the true friends of the people . . ."

He spoke at length. It helped sustain him in his resistance; and possibly he hoped to convince Saint Just.

Moreover, of what consequence would a victory be which gave him power but at the same time destroyed the tribune? As an orator, as a man of public assemblies, he could not conceive of a government without speeches. He was a lawyer. The hour of consuls and pretorians had not yet struck for France.

And another thing restrained him—the inactivity of the Jacobins.

He remembered the meeting of the night before, the tears of his audience, the cry of David, amid the cheering:

"We will drink hemlock with thee!"

Promises, applause, protestations, and what had they all amounted to?

"And Couthon?" he asked, suddenly.

"He is waiting at home," said Payan, "until you send for him."

Robespierre the Younger wrote: "Couthon, all patriots are outlawed; the entire people are in arms; it would be treachery for you not to hasten to the Commune, where we are." Maximilien and Saint Just signed it.

Couthon promptly had himself carried there. He smiled and stretched out his arms to his friends. Then Robespierre rose and spoke. His words threw the Council into

OUTSIDE THE HÔTEL DE VILLE
During the Uprising of the 9th Thermidor

feverish excitement. He spared nothing, named those who must be seized by the throat, to protect the Assembly and save the Revolution. They were: Collot d'Herbois, Amar, Léonard Bourdon, Dubarron, Fréron, Tallien, Carnot, Panis, Dubois-Crancé, Vadier, Javogue, Fouché, Cranet and Moyse Bayle.

"Rascals," he cried, "do not hope for mercy from us. Mercy would be equivalent to sharing in your crimes. You have raised the poniard against us. But it is not that we wish to avenge. No. Your conspiracy is execrable because in attacking the inviolable persons of its representatives you oppress the people itself, and in violating the protection of the law, you violate France and mankind."

These words aroused his audience. There was a general embracing, shaking of hands, cries that the Republic was saved. But of what use was this? Would it not have been better to exhort the undecided Sections who were waiting outside the Hôtel de Ville, in the Place de Grève? At this time a word from Maximilien would still have hurled them against the Tuileries.

All those around their leader felt this, and said so. He refused obstinately. If he did not act immediately, it was the end of him and his followers. Time passed. Robespierre resumed his speech.

Meanwhile, what was the Convention doing? It had finally become somewhat aware of its danger and had just appointed Barras general of the troops to defend the law. But where were these troops? Deputies, preceded and followed by torch bearers, rushed to all the Sections, trying to drum Parisians out of their beds. The municipal officers did the same. The result was that the hostile emissaries of the Convention and the Commune, surrounded by their smoking torches, confronted each other in the darkness. But only the world of night prowlers appeared. These, coming from the faubourg Saint Martin and skulking from street to street, finally arrived at La Grève, where they lay in wait. They were the friends of Jacques Roux. Up above, behind the high windows, under the lights of the chandeliers, Robespierre in his blue coat and nankeen breeches was polishing his phrases, while below, creeping along the walls, these mysterious men were plying his artillery men with wine.

Robespierre continued to speak. It seemed as if he were making up for his enforced silence at the Convention.

And now, at the corner of the Rue de la Vannerie appeared men decorated in tricolored sashes: the emissaries of the Convention. From one street corner to another they stopped and read by torchlight the decree of outlawry.

THE NATIONAL CONVENTION

> after hearing the report of its Committee of Public Safety and Committee of General Surety, prohibits closing the gates of entry or convoking the Sections without an authorization from the Committees of Public Safety and General Surety.
>
> It declares outlawed all those public officials who

> give orders to an armed force to advance against the National Convention or who ignore its decrees.
>
> It also outlaws those individuals against whom a warrant of arrest and accusation has been promulgated and who either have not complied with the law or have fled.

This decree struck Paris dumb. Hardly had it been proclaimed by the agents of the Committees when the streets were deserted. The curious who had still lingered hastened to their homes, some of them tossing their weapons into the gutters. And soon the dense mob of rioting patriots which had packed La Grève began to melt away. On seeing this, the Commune caused the arrest of the emissaries. The decree was seized. Then Mayor Floriot-Lescot had the fatal idea of reading it in mockery to all those who had collected in the galleries and who had no idea of the impending danger. Now the decree, promulgated against whoever supported the Commune, declared death without trial for all. The councillors paled at the thought. Many rushed for the doors.

In a short time we were a small group of only fifty determined men. It was about one-thirty when it was decided we should move to a room in the secretariat. The corridors were thronged with strangers. Friends? Traitors? Nobody knew. After all our enthusiasm, lassitude began to possess us.

Outside it was worse. The defenders of the Commune were dispersing. Cannoneers and national guardsmen, who had remained there inactive since seven o'clock, were tired of waiting. A few of them quietly slipped out of the ranks, while bolder ones made off to the cabarets. After hearing the decree, the officers themselves relaxed vigilance, lost confidence. They tolerated everything, even closing their eyes to desertion. When this was observed, it was decided to illuminate the façade with lanterns, in order to keep a better watch of the crowd. It was a strange sight, this festive illumination on this tragic night. At two o'clock an entire battalion deserted.

Meanwhile in the chamber of Equality where we had gathered a man sat writing. When he had finished he handed the paper to his neighbor, Saint Just. The latter had not slept for two days. He remained calm, cold, elegant.

Voices floated up from La Grève, shouting, "Vive Robespierre!" In the corridors a violent brawl burst out; men were running heavily. The noise drew nearer, rose with a kind of slow and terrible fury, as if the besieged were yielding the stairway one step at a time. Confused shouts mingled with the clash of weapons. Blows from the butt-ends of muskets crashed against the partitions.

We were silent. Torches lit up the faces of pale, motionless men, who sat listening. A door in the adjoining room gave way to the blows, as if rent asunder. One of the unseen defenders shouted with all his might:

"Vive Robespierre! Vive la Commune!"

We heard a body crash to the floor and at the same time voices yelling:

THE ATTACK ON ROBESPIERRE AND HIS FOLLOWERS.
According to this print Robespierre was shot and did not attempt suicide.

"Vive la Convention! Death to traitors! Down with the tyrant!"

They hurled themselves against our door. All of us, standing in an attitude of defiance, stared at the wooden door where death knocked. It gave way and fell with a crash within the room.

Suddenly, among us, a pistol rang out.

Maximilien lunged forward across the table. He had fired upon himself and had broken his jaw-bone. He had missed his aim. Blood flooded his mouth and poured down his cheek.

We rushed to him and picked him up, as grenadiers burst in pell-mell, yelling like fiends. Among them, Léonard Bourdon, disheveled, dirty, foul with sweat, points his sword at those of us whom he must first arrest. A window is opened. Augustin Robespierre leaps out, runs along the cornice. Shall I follow him? I see him beat the air with his arms, lean forward and fall, whirling, while a prolonged shout rises from the illuminated square. I turn back, sick with terror. The room is packed with a screaming mob. Some of the councillors are thrown to the ground, trampled underfoot. Lebas has been killed. Henriot, lowering his head like a wild boar, rushes upon his assailants, bowls them over and runs blindly into the corridors. Lerebours and Coffinhal, desperate, upset a table, push me, drag me along. We slip through a little door. Running, we pass through two rooms filled with shadows. Lerebours knows the building. He precedes us with a sure step; he closes and bolts two or three doors.

A deserted staircase, a long corridor lighted by an oil lamp, a grille, then a high door, with a small window and a latch. Now we are in the street. Thick night conceals our exit. I am saved.

CHAPTER TWELVE

OUTSIDE, it was raining. The distant lights of La Grève gleamed in the puddles and on the wet cannon. Singing men were running through Rue Antoine and along the quais. Sabers flashed; flags waved. And the rain fell, like a curtain, on the night of the 9th of Thermidor.

CHAPTER THIRTEEN

It became known throughout Paris that at dawn Robespierre had been carried to the Convention and that Thuriot had refused him entrance. From the earliest bulletins I learned that my friend was kept under observation in a chamber of the Committee of Public Safety. It was said that he was at the point of death.

I felt a kind of shame at having abandoned him in this cruel moment. But what supreme duty could I render the dying? Follow him? Die with him? These are sacrifices demanded less by the loyalty of friendship than by the honor of a partisan. If I had espoused the cause of Maximilien, approved his acts, without doubt, like his brother and Lebas I should have wished to share his fate.

But on the contrary, had I not at the time of Danton's trial exerted myself to the limit against fratricidal hate? Had I not braved his cold determination to treat all his opponents as rascals—that determination which brought on murders, led to Prairial, and later on was to form the conspiracy of fear against the pitiless chief, the judicial dictator.

This hour had come. Should I now expiate my all too exact prophecy by a sacrifice which would deny it?

Absurd as this seemed to me, I none the less hurried to the offices of the Committee. Friendship, pity, the power of memory, were stronger than reason. Since my friend was there, dying, I would go to give him my hand; I would help him in the pain of death.

It was about eight o'clock. The rain had washed and freshened the sky. There were few people in the neighborhood of the Tuileries, but the halls, on the contrary, were crowded. Without difficulty I found the room where Maximilien lay. Crowds of curious passed in and out. I could hear much talking—nothing but jeers, vile insults, the cowardly banter of those who abuse the dying.

"Your majesty is suffering?"

"What? Has our Incorruptible at last lost his voice?"

"It's his turn now to stick his head through the little slot."

"There he is with his hair dressed like a nun's."

Then an authoritative voice, that of Lacoste, commanding:

"Tell the surgeon to dress his wound carefully, so that he will be in fit condition to take his punishment."

I could no longer hold back. Elbowing my way through the crowd, I entered. Maximilien, stretched out on a long table, was hatless, collarless, and his half-open shirt was dyed with blood.

A cannoneer approached him.

"He's dead," he announced.

"No," said an employee of the Committee, "he is still breathing."

Then Legendre entered.

"Well, tyrant," he said, with braggadocio, "the whole Republic was not big enough for you yesterday, but today you take up hardly more than two feet on this little table!"

Thus the butcher had his revenge—he whom Robespierre had so many times crushed with a look, thrown him to one side, like a stuck bull. All laughed coarsely at his remark. Legendre caught my eye, hesitated as to what he should do or say, and then, seeing me endure the gaze, he did not know what to think, and wandered off.

I stayed there a half hour, mingling with the clerks and the soldiers. Maximilien did not open his eyes; he seemed to be in the heavy sleep of the wounded, drained of all his blood, ready to yield up his soul.

They placed a pine deal box, open at one side, under his head. He was inert. However, as a ray of sunlight struck his face, he covered his eyes with his arm, with the gesture of a sleeping man. For two hours these scoundrels had been tugging at his arm. Now one of them said:

"He's not dead. He's still warm."

And another voice, besotted, sinister:

"They should have dumped him into the sewer."

Something called the stragglers into the room outside. I then drew near and bent over him. Near at hand his face seemed to have the pallor of death. He showed life only by feeble involuntary contractions. I spoke clearly, asking I do not remember what, but loud enough for him to recognize my voice. I waited. No response, not a

ROBESPIERRE LYING WOUNDED AT THE HÔTEL DE VILLE.

quiver. Then I departed, assured like everyone else that the wounded man would not survive his pistol shot more than another hour or so.

All were mistaken. I was to learn that shortly after my departure, at the moment when it was least expected, Maximilien had suddenly arisen and had staggered to an armchair.

From now on he was spared nothing. Due to someone's cruel whimsy, he was dragged off to the Hotel Dieu, and then to the Conciergerie. Those who conducted him there halted the procession at every street corner. At the *quai des Lunettes* the armchair was put down on the sidewalk and the man who yesterday was all-powerful was now subjected to the mockery of the rabble. He shrugged his shoulders. They carried him off and, bloody as he was, threw him into a cell until evening—until the time when, Fouquier-Tinville having established the identity of the proscribed, the journey to Calvary began.

I FOLLOWED the tumbril from the Rue de la Ferronnerie to the Place de la Revolution. I was not separated from it until the last moments, and then by a barrier of horsemen, who kept the curious back from the scaffold.

Like his companions, Maximilien was shackled to the sides of the cart. I looked only at him. My eyes, burning with tears, were fixed on that suffering face, whose features still recalled my tenderest memories—that face I now saw bound with a bloody cloth.

The jolting of the cart wrung deep groans from Couthon,

from Augustin, from Henriot. But Robespierre, firm, silent, sat bolt upright. All one could discern upon his face was a look of revulsion. Due to the change in his appearance caused by his black, blood-clotted hair, clipped short over his forehead, it was difficult to recognize him.

From time to time a few ghastly buffoons, clinging from ladders, would vomit forth abuse upon him. Maximilien, shrugging his shoulders, would stare at them with set and glittering eyes. The tumbril creaked on stubbornly, lurching over the uneven pavement.

The course through Rue Saint Honoré lasted a long hour. What a memory! This macabre bacchanale, the hideous yells of the depraved, the profane and blood-drenched pomp, the venal fury—no, nothing can describe it. Never before was a mob so base, so vile.

From where did they come, these men at every street corner, who rushed out howling at the vanquished? A thousand whores, hidden away for five years, issued forth with their rouge, their feathers, and their fans, to strut before their windows, screaming:

"To the guillotine!"

They wore bouquets of flowers between their breasts and held up their painted mouths for men to kiss. One of them in an evening dress, leaning over the sides of the tumbril, spat on the condemned. The balconies applauded. Everything was permitted, the soldiers of the escort mingling their curses with those of the rabble.

A halt was called before the Duplay house. A group of furies who had been gathered there in advance, clasped hands, and singing, danced round the cartload of dying men. Then a boy appeared, with a butcher's bucket and a broom. A jet of fresh blood splashed against the house. Maximilien closed his eyes. He did not open them again until the cart had passed the iron fence of the *Conception*.

Finally, he seemed to become aware of my presence. He leaned toward the cart-wheel and saw me. My distracted face was turned toward him. He inclined his head twice as if to thank me. His eyes, already dimmed by the shadows of eternity, gazed toward me with a grave and tender farewell and closed. I could not hold back my tears. A national guardsman thrust me to one side, cursing. But now the cortège turned and halted beside the scaffold. They were at the threshold of death. Only Saint Just and Maximilien could clamber up the steps unassisted. The bodies of the others were bruised and broken.

It was hideous. A butchery. Henriot appeared first and sticky with mud and gore was strapped to the plank. His left eye dangled over his cheek, and the executioner plucked it away. Couthon had to be guillotined crosswise, after they had in vain tried to wrench his poor paralyzed body into position. Drunk with cruelty the mob howled. But it was strangely mute when Saint Just, wrapped in mystery and haughty silence died without a smile, with the disdain of marble.

Robespierre was pushed forward. A deep roar rose from the vast multitude. It was now some time after six, and the setting sun reddened the foliage of the trees. The

Seine flowed past gently like a flood of blue silk. The bloody knife hung ready. Suddenly the executioner's attendant slipped up behind Maximilien and in one jerk stripped off the bandage which bound his poor, wounded jaw. His mouth yawned open with its loose teeth. The scream of a tortured beast pierced the square. His face appeared with its mad eyes. Long enough never to forget it we stared at this twisted, gaping face a broken man with bound arms held out ardently toward the knife.

The crowd shouted. I saw a horse rear, a plank tilt forward. In my terror I hid my eyes in my bent arm, like a child.

Before the knife fell, the whole square gasped as in one breath. Then came an immense uproar. Everyone, citizens, citizenesses, *Sans-Culottes* and soldiers, deputies and policemen, all those who had come to see the death of the Revolution and who understood nothing, all uttered a shout of acclamation which rose in endless waves. It was still ringing in my ears when, like a hunted man, I fled from the square.

THE END

THIS BOOK WAS DESIGNED BY ROBERT S. JOSEPHY
AND PRINTED UNDER HIS SUPERVISION BY THE
J. J. LITTLE & IVES COMPANY, NEW YORK